Daily *warm-ups*

PREFIXES, SUFFIXES, & ROOTS

Ruth Rice

WALCH PUBLISHING

1   2   3   4   5   6   7   8   9   10

ISBN 0-8251-4960-6

Copyright © 2004

Walch Publishing

P. O. Box 658 • Portland, Maine 04104-0658

walch.com

Printed in the United States of America

The *Daily Warm-Ups* series is a wonderful way to turn extra classroom minutes into valuable learning time. The 180 quick activities—one for each day of the school year—review, practice, and teach English prefixes, suffixes, and roots. These daily activities may be used at the very beginning of class to get students into learning mode, near the end of class to make good educational use of that transitional time, in the middle of class to shift gears between lessons—or whenever else you have minutes that now go unused. In addition to providing students with fascinating information, they are a natural path to other classroom activities involving critical thinking.

Daily Warm-Ups are easy-to-use reproducibles—simply photocopy the day's activity and distribute it. Or make a transparency of the activity and project it on the board. You may want to use the activities for extra-credit points or as a check on critical-thinking skills and problem-solving skills.

However you choose to use them, *Daily Warm-Ups* are a convenient and useful supplement to your regular lesson plans. Make every minute of your class time count!

Pretest: Roots Part I

In each word below, the root appears in bold. Match each root with its meaning from the list by writing the correct letter on each line. (*Hint:* Do not think of the meaning of the entire word, just the root.) Take a guess if you do not know. There will be one letter choice left over.

___ 1. in**cred**ible

___ 2. e**duc**ate

___ 3. **geo**graphy

___ 4. re**ject**

___ 5. **man**ipulate

a. earth

b. bird

c. hand

d. believe

e. lead

f. throw

1

Pretest: Roots Part II

In each word below, the prefix appears in bold. Match each prefix with its meaning from the list by writing the correct letter on each line. (*Hint*: Do not think of the meaning of the entire word, just the prefix.) Take a guess if you do not know. There will be one letter choice left over.

___ 1. centi**pede**   a. life

___ 2. **photo**graph   b. light

___ 3. dis**tort**   c. sound

___ 4. sur**vive**   d. foot

___ 5. tele**phone**   e. body

          f. turn, twist

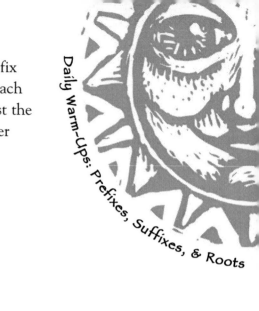

2

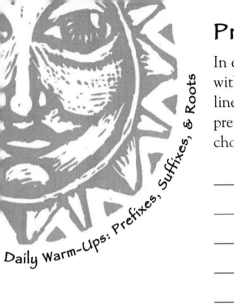

Pretest: Prefixes Part 1

In each word below, the prefix appears in bold. Match each prefix with its meaning from the list by writing the correct letter on each line. (*Hint:* Do not think of the meaning of the entire word, just the prefix.) Take a guess if you do not know. There will be one letter choice left over.

____ 1. **para**phrase

____ 2. **per**forate

____ 3. **hypo**dermic

____ 4. **intra**mural

____ 5. **neo**classic

a. within

b. through

c. out of

d. under

e. similar

f. new

3

Pretest: Prefixes Part II

In each word below, the prefix appears in bold. Match each prefix with its meaning from the list by writing the correct letter on each line. (*Hint:* Do not think of the meaning of the entire word, just the prefix.) Take a guess if you do not know. There will be one letter choice left over.

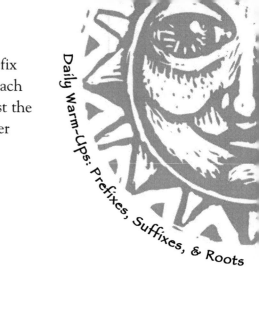

____ 1. **bene**fit

____ 2. **contra**dict

____ 3. **kilo**watt

____ 4. **post**pone

____ 5. **trans**fer

a. against

b. good

c. after

d. 1,000

e. above

f. across

4

Pretest: Suffixes Part I

Each bold suffix below changes the basic word into a different part of speech. On each line, write **noun** (names something), **verb** (shows action, tells what the noun does), **adjective** (describes a noun), or **adverb** (describes a verb) to show the part of speech of each word after the suffix is added.

_____   1. steri**lize**

_____   2. firm**ness**

_____   3. slow**ly**

_____   4. recep**tive**

_____   5. dus**ty**

_____   6. joy**ous**

5

Pretest: Suffixes Part II

Each bold suffix below changes the basic word into a different part of speech. On each line, write **noun** (names something), **verb** (shows action, tells what the noun does), **adjective** (describes a noun), or **adverb** (describes a verb) to show the part of speech of each word after the suffix is added.

_____ 1. hesi**tate**

_____ 2. friend**ship**

_____ 3. back**ward**

_____ 4. engine**er**

_____ 5. atten**tion**

_____ 6. dur**able**

6

Picturing Roots 1

Each of the drawings below suggests a root word. Study the drawings, and match each with the correct root from the box below.

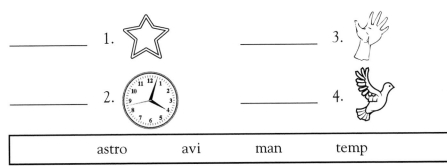

_____ 1. ☆

_____ 2. 🕐

_____ 3. ✋

_____ 4. 🕊

| astro | avi | man | temp |

Now think of a word that uses one of the roots you used above. Use that word in a complete sentence.

7

Picturing Roots II

Each of the drawings below suggests a root word. Study the drawings, and match each with the correct root from the box below.

_____ 1.

_____ 2.

_____ 3.

_____ 4.

| biblio | geo | homo | photo |

Now think of a word that uses one of the roots you used above. Use that word in a complete sentence.

8

Picturing Roots III

Each of the drawings below suggests a root word. Study the drawings, and match each with the correct root from the box below.

_____ 1. *Four score and seven years ago*

_____ 2.

_____ 3.

_____ 4.

hort	ped	scrip	zo

Now think of a word that uses one of the roots you used above. Use that word in a complete sentence.

9

Ducks All Around 1

Did you know that the ancient Romans turned a flock of "ducks" loose and that they are all around us every day? These "ducks" are actually words containing the root *duc* (*duct, duce*) from the Latin word *ducere* (to lead). The shortest word we have from this root is *duct* (a tube).

Think of some other words that have the root *duc*. List five below. (There are actually several hundred words formed from this root!) Study the words, and circle any prefixes or suffixes that have been added to the root *duc*. Then use one of your words in a complete sentence.

10

Ducks All Around 11

Recall that the root *duc* (*duct, duce*) comes from the Latin word *ducere* (to lead). Even though many specialized words have been formed with *duc*, its basic meaning is retained. This fact can help you figure out the meaning of words containing *duc* from context.

Below, form words by adding a prefix, a suffix, or both to the root *duc*. The definitions of the words are given. Use a dictionary, if necessary.

1. __ duc __ __ __   to teach

2. __ __ duc __ __ __   decreasing

3. __ __ __ duct   something manufactured

4. __ __ __ __ __ duc __   to present one person to another so they can become acquainted

Now use one of the words above in a complete sentence.

11

Ducks All Around III

Recall that the root *duc* (*duct*, *duce*) comes from the Latin word *ducere* (to lead).

Below, form words by adding a prefix, a suffix, or both to the root *duc*. The definitions of the words are given. Use a dictionary, if necessary.

1. _ _ _ duct _ _   one who leads an orchestra

2. _ _ duc _ _ _ _   the act of taking away

3. _ _ duce _ _ _ _   a motive; a purpose for doing something

4. duct _ _ _ _   without tubes (such as certain glands in the human body)

12

There are many examples of words with the root *duc* that contain more than one prefix or more than one suffix, such as *inductivism*. Think of another example, and list it below. Use a dictionary if you need help.

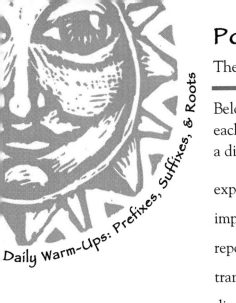

Port I

The root *port* means *to carry*.

Below is a list of words that each contain the root *port* and a prefix. For each word, add different suffixes to make at least three new words. Use a dictionary if you need help. The first one has been done for you.

export   <u>exporter, exportable, exportation</u>

import   _____

report   _____

transport   _____

disport   _____

comport   _____

Now use three of the words you formed above in a short paragraph.

13

Port II

Recall that the root *port* means *to carry*. Many words containing *port* also contain a prefix. Some words, such as *portage*, only use a suffix with the root *port*.

Think of some other words that contain the root *port* with only a suffix. Use a dictionary if you need help. List at least three words below with their definitions. Then write a complete sentence using one of the words you listed.

14

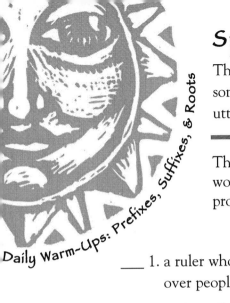

Speaking of Roots 1

The root *dic* or *dict* means *to say*. You may already be familiar with some words containing the root *dic*, such as *dictation*, the act of uttering words.

The words listed below all contain the root *dic* or *dict*. Match each word with its definition by writing the correct letter in the space provided. Use a dictionary if you need help.

___ 1. a ruler who has total authority and power over people

___ 2. to foretell the future

___ 3. to charge someone with a crime; to accuse

___ 4. to disagree with; to speak against

a. contradict

b. dictator

c. indict

d. predict

Now use one of the words in a sentence of your own.

15

© 2004 Walch Publishing

Speaking of Roots II

Recall that the root *dic* or *dict* means *to say*. You may already be familiar with some words containing the root *dic*, such as *dictation*, the act of uttering words.

The words listed below all contain the root *dic* or *dict*. Match each word with its definition by writing the correct letter in the space provided. Use a dictionary if you need help.

____ 1. a book of words and their definitions   a. benediction

____ 2. a blessing   b. dictionary

____ 3. a curse   c. malediction

____ 4. the student with the highest rank in a graduating class   d. valedictorian

Now use one of the words in a sentence of your own.

16

Speaking of Roots III

Recall that the root *dic* or *dict* means *to say*. In the space below, write the prefixes used in *malediction* and *benediction*. Then write the meaning for each prefix. How do these prefixes change the meaning of the root word? Think of another set of words in which this occurs, and write the words below.

17

Seeing Roots 1

The roots *scope*, *vid* or *vis*, and *spec* or *spic* all mean *see* or *look*. You may be familiar with some words containing these roots, such as *microscope*, *visualize*, and *inspection*.

Decide which of these roots fits into the incomplete word in each sentence below. Use a dictionary if you need help.

1. Something that is **con_____uous** is easy to see.

2. A person who is **circum_____t** is cautious and looks around before proceeding with something.

3. A **peri_____** is used in a submarine to see above the surface of the water.

4. A **_____eotape** is used to record visual images and sound.

5. If you like interesting colors and shapes, you will enjoy looking through a **kaleido_____**.

18

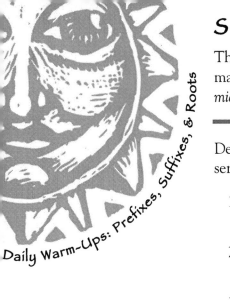

Seeing Roots II

The roots *scope*, *vid* or *vis*, and *spec* or *spic* all mean *see* or *look*. You may be familiar with some words containing these roots, such as *microscope*, *visualize*, and *inspection*.

Decide which of these roots fits into the incomplete word in each sentence below. Use a dictionary if you need help.

1. If you have a good **per_____tive,** you see things as they really are and recognize their relative importance.

2. With a **radar_____,** airports can direct air traffic and prevent collisions.

3. A _____**ta** is a broad view.

4. A **horo_____** forecasts your future through the analysis of the positions of the heavenly bodies.

5. The _____**trum** is the group of colors you see when a ray of light is broken up by a prism.

19

Seeing Roots III

The roots *scope*, *vid* or *vis*, and *spec* or *spic* all mean *see* or *look*. You may be familiar with some words containing these roots, such as *microscope*, *visualize*, and *inspection*.

Decide which of these roots fits into the incomplete word in each sentence below. Use a dictionary if you need help.

1. With a **gastro_____**, a doctor can observe what is going on inside a person's stomach.

2. A _____**ionary** is a dreamy, idealistic person who sees things differently from the way others do.

3. A _____**ter** is a visible ghost.

4. E_____**ence** is something brought into court to help a jury determine a verdict.

5. A _____**or** is a flap on a helmet that can be raised to allow the wearer to see.

20

Roots Starting with "V" 1

Julius Caesar said, "Veni, vidi, vici," which means "I came, I saw, I conquered." These words have formed the basis of many modern words. And so have the roots *ver* (true), *viv* or *vita* (life), and *voc* or *vok* (call or voice).

In the following paragraph, choose a root to complete each word. Use the roots *ven* (come), *vid* or *vis* (see), *vic* or *vinc* (conquer) in addition to *ver*, *viv*, or *vita*, and *voc* or *vok* (defined above). Definitions of the words are given in parentheses.

Joe said, "I wish I could have a real ad__ __ __ture (exciting experience) like the knights of the Middle Ages. It must have been exciting to __ __ __ture (go) forth to slay dragons and rescue fair damsels. I am con__ __ __ __ed (persuaded) that I am living in the wrong period of history. Maybe if I watch this __ __ __eotape (visual recording) movie about King Arthur's court, I can __ __ __ualize (see) myself as an in__ __ __ __ible (unconquerable) knight gaining a __ __ __tory (win) over an enemy horde storming the castle. I can just hear my men shouting so loudly that they strain their __ __ __al (of the voice) chords as they send their spears flying.

21

© 2004 Walch Publishing

Roots Starting with "V" II

In the following paragraph, decide which root to put into each word. The roots you will use are *ven* (come), *vid* or *vis* (see), *vic* or *vinc* (conquer) in addition to *ver* (true), *viv* or *vita (life)*, and *voc* or *vok* (call or voice). Definitions of the words are given in parentheses.

"To follow the __ __ __ation (occupation) of knighthood," said Joe, one must have a great deal of __ __ __ __lity (pep). I take __ __ __ __min pills (food substances essential for life) every day and get lots of sleep and exercise, but I wonder if I could sur__ __ __e (exist) as a knight. I wish we could re__ __ __e (bring back to life) the old days and relive some of the pages of history. Instead I will just make an a__ __ __ation (hobby) out of reading about the age of chivalry, and in my mind's eye, I will en__ __ __ion (see) those exciting events. The library, which is __ __ __ible (able to be seen) from my window, is a __ __ __itable (real, true) storehouse of information, and it can help me __ __ __ify (establish the truth) the facts.

22

Down to the Root 1

tract: a root meaning *to draw or pull*

Underline the root in each word below. Then write the definition of each word that includes the meaning of the root.

contract   detract   extract   retract   tractor
contractor   distracted   protracted   traction

Down to the Root II

tract: a root meaning *to draw or pull*

Choose the word that best completes each sentence.

contract   detract   traction
contractor   distracted   tractor

1. After Dan's father had an accident while riding his _____, he had to give up farming for the rest of the season.

2. When he was released from the hospital, he had to have his leg in _____ for several weeks.

3. Dan's father watched television and read a great deal to help keep himself _____ from the pain and boredom.

4. His brother, a _____, visited him often.

Now write a sentence using the words not used in the sentences above.

24

Down to the Root III

mit or *miss*: a root meaning *to send*

Underline the root in each word below. Then write the definition of each word that includes the meaning of the root.

committed   missile   omitted   remission   transmission

dismissed   missive   permit   remit

25

Down to the Root IV

mit or *miss*: a root meaning *to send*

Choose the word that best completes each sentence.

committed   permit   remit
dismissed   remission   transmission

1. Jen was so excited when she received a long-awaited
   _____ to drive a car.

2. Her excitement quickly turned to disappointment because the
   car's _____ was out of order.

3. Jen then _____ the whole idea
   of going for a ride.

4. She _____ herself to working
   hard to buy her own car.

26

Now write a sentence using the words not used in the sentences above.

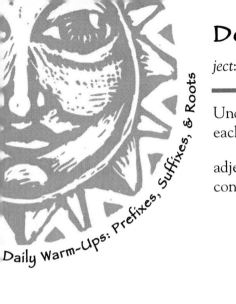

Down to the Root V

ject: a root meaning *to throw*

Underline the root in each word below. Then write the definition of each word that includes the meaning of the root.

adjective dejected injected project reject

conjecture eject interjection projectile

27

Down to the Root VI

ject: a root meaning *to throw*

Choose the word that best completes each sentence.

adjective   eject   projectile
dejected   project   reject

1. Jonathan failed the English test because he didn't know that a(n) _____ describes a noun.

2. He sometimes felt _____ when he received a bad grade on a test.

3. However, when his father asked him to work on a science _____, he cheered up.

4. Working with his dad was not an opportunity Jonathan wanted to _____.

Now write a sentence using the words not used in the sentences above.

28

Down to the Root VII

flu: a root meaning *to flow*

Underline the root in each word below. Then write the definition of each word that includes the meaning of the root.

affluent	fluid	flume	influx	superfluous
fluctuate	fluent	flush	mellifluous	

29

Down to the Root VIII

flu: a root meaning *to flow*

Choose the word that best completes each sentance.

affluent	fluent	influx
fluctuate	flume	superfluous

1. Because the prices of stocks _____ a great deal, it is difficult to know what to buy and what to sell.

2. Some people have become extremely _____ from buying and selling stocks.

3. Knowledge of the stock market takes a constant _____ of information on which to base decisions.

4. Learning about the stock market is like being _____ in a foreign language.

Now write a sentence using the words not used in the sentences above.

Down to the Root IX

flex: a root meaning *to bend*

Underline the root in each word below. Then write the definition of each word that includes the meaning of the root.

deflect   flexible   flexuous   genuflected   reflex

flexed   flexor   inflection   reflection

31

Down to the Root X

flex: a root meaning *to bend*

Choose the word that best completes each sentence.

deflect	flexible	genuflect
flexed	inflection	reflection

1. It is said that Narcissus stared at his _____ in a pool of water.

2. The body builder _____ the muscles in her arms.

3. The slight _____ in the teacher's voice revealed his southern roots.

4. The firefighter tried to _____ attention away from the victim.

Now write a sentence using the words not used in the sentences above.

32

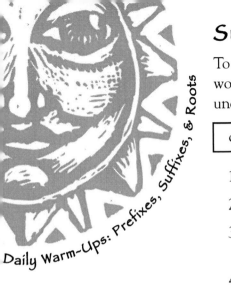

Supplying Roots 1

To the right of each item below is the definition of the incomplete word. In each definition, the meaning of the missing root is underlined. Use the roots in the box to fill in the lines.

chron	ject	pac	voc	chrom	ven

1. con __ __ __ tion—a meeting or <u>coming</u> together

2. __ __ __ __ __ atics—the branch of science that deals with <u>color</u>

3. inter __ __ __ __ ion—a word or remark <u>thrown</u> in between others

4. __ __ __ ifier—an object given to a baby to keep it <u>peaceful</u> and quiet.

5. syn __ __ __ __ __ ize—to set to occur at the same <u>time</u>

6. __ __ __ ation—a person's <u>calling</u> (his or her occupation)

In the space below, write a sentence of your own using at least two of the words defined above.

33

Supplying Roots II

To the right of each item below is the definition of the incomplete word. In each definition, the meaning of the missing root is underlined. Use the roots in the box to fill in the lines.

scrib	nov	derm	fid	mort	mit	soph

1. re __ __ __ tance—money that is <u>sent</u> back

2. __ __ __ __ istry—<u>wise</u>-sounding, but misleading reasoning

3. epi __ __ __ __ is—the outer layer of the <u>skin</u>

4. __ __ __ __ __ ble—to <u>write</u> marks that don't mean anything

5. re __ __ __ ate—to make <u>new</u> or restore to a former state

6. __ __ __ __ ification—humiliation so great you wish you were <u>dead</u>

7. con __ __ __ ant(e)—a person you can <u>trust</u> with your secrets

In the space below, write a sentence of your own using at least two of the words defined above.

Supplying Roots III

To the right of each item below is the definition of the incomplete word. In each definition, the meaning of the missing root is underlined. Use the roots in the box to fill in the lines.

meter	avi	man	mort

1. __ __ __ uscript—something written by <u>hand</u>

2. sphygmomano __ __ __ __ __—an instrument used by a doctor to <u>measure</u> blood pressure

3. __ __ __ __ ician—an undertaker (one who embalms <u>dead</u> persons)

4. __ __ __ ary—a place where <u>birds</u> are kept

Choose one of the roots above, and list as many words as possible that contain that root.

Supplying Roots IV

To the right of each item below is the definition of the incomplete word. In each definition, the meaning of the missing root is underlined. Use the roots in the box to fill in the lines.

photo	agro	phone	astro

1. _ _ _ _ _ nomical—enormous in number, such as the <u>stars</u> in the sky

2. _ _ _ _ _ nomist—a person who studies the management of farmlands (<u>fields</u>)

3. _ _ _ _ _ tropism—the tendency of plants to turn toward the <u>light</u>

4. _ _ _ _ _ tics—the study of <u>sounds</u> employed in speaking

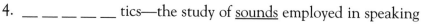

Choose one of the roots above, and list as many words as possible that contain that root.

36

Supplying Roots V

To the right of each item below is the definition of the incomplete word. In each definition, the meaning of the missing root is underlined. Use the roots in the box to fill in the lines.

soph	ped	spec	script

1. __ __ __ estal—the <u>foot</u> or base on which a statue stands

2. tran __ __ __ __ __ t—a copy of something, such as a typewritten copy of <u>written</u> notes

3. __ __ __ __ isticated—appears to be <u>wise</u> in the ways of the world.

4. __ __ __ __ tator—a person who <u>looks</u> but doesn't take part in some activity or sport

---

Choose one of the roots above, and list as many words as possible that contain that root.

37

Supplying Roots VI

In each pair of sentences below, the same root is missing from the incomplete words. The definitions of the words are given at the ends of the sentences. Use these clues to fill in the lines.

1. At the end of my term paper, I made a __ __ __ __iography. (a list of books used in preparing the paper)

   Jonah was the __ __ __ __ical character who was swallowed by a whale. (pertaining to the Judeo-Christian scriptures)

2. I shall try to in__ __ __porate that idea in the text. (include it in the main body of material)

   The head of the __ __ __pse was found in the river by the police. (dead body)

Find at least two more words for each root used in the above sentences. Using your dictionary, provide a brief definition, and use the words in a sentence.

38

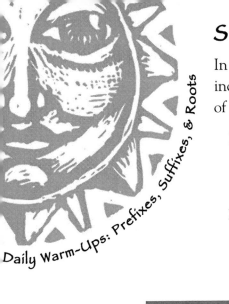

Supplying Roots VII

In each pair of sentences below, the same root is missing from the incomplete words. The definitions of the words are given at the ends of the sentences. Use these clues to fill in the lines.

1. For the __ __ __ale, the band played a special number. (end of the performance)

   We must __ __ __alize our plans. (complete)

2. De__ __ __ __ated foods require less space for storage. (from which the water has been removed)

   In Switzerland, much __ __ __ __oelectric power is generated. (water power)

Find at least two more words for each root used in the above sentences. Using your dictionary, provide a brief definition, and use the words in a sentence.

39

Supplying Roots VIII

In each pair of sentences below, the same root is missing from the incomplete words. The definitions of the words are given at the ends of the sentences. Use these clues to fill in the lines.

1. Even persons with severe mental illness sometimes have __ __ __id moments. (clear, bright, enlightened)

   Certain types of objects are made of __ __ __ite. (a type of clear plastic)

2. Caterpillars undergo a trans__ __ __ation when they become butterflies. (complete change)

   These laws are im__ __ __able. (unchangeable)

40

Find at least two more words for each root used in the above sentences. Using your dictionary, provide a brief definition of each word, and use the words in a sentence.

Supplying Roots IX

In each pair of sentences below, the same root is missing from the incomplete words. The definitions of the words are given at the ends of the sentences. Use these clues to fill in the lines.

1. The __ __ __es and chromosomes are arranged in certain patterns in the cells in our bodies. (the elements that determined our characteristics at birth)

    I felt re__ __ __erated after a month's retreat in the mountains. (reborn)

2. Life could be described as a __ __ __ __uous road. (twisting, turning)

    He is a con__ __ __ __ionist in the circus. (a person who can bend and twist into strange positions)

Find at least two more words for each root used in the above sentences. Using your dictionary, provide a brief definition of each word, and use the words in a sentence.

41

Defining Derived Words 1

In each sentence below, a root is in bold. Look up the root to find its meaning. Then figure out what the entire word means. Write the definition for the word, underlining the definition of the root. You may want to use a dictionary.

Example: It is **evid**ent that he is lying. **Definition:** easy to <u>see</u>

1. We must **ver**ify this statement. **Definition:**

2. This artist uses very **viv**id colors. **Definition:**

3. Outer space is in**fin**ite. **Definition:**

42

List more examples of words with these roots in the space below. If you do not know the definitions of your examples, look them up in the dictionary. Notice the similarities between the definitions of the words with the same root.

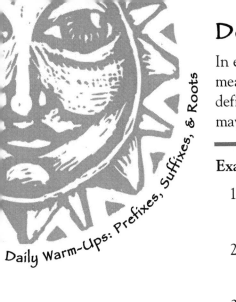

Defining Derived Words II

In each sentence below, a root is in bold. Look up the root to find its meaning. Then figure out what the entire word means. Write the definition for the word, underlining the definition of the root. You may want to use a dictionary.

Example: It is e**vid**ent that he is lying. ***Definition:*** easy to <u>see</u>

1. In the word *cook*, the letters *c* and *k* are **homo**phones.

   Definition:

2. Algae and certain other plants are **hydro**phytes.

   Definition:

3. At one time, people believed in the **geo**centric theory of the universe.

   Definition:

List more examples of words with these roots in the space below. If you do not know the definitions of your examples, look them up in the dictionary. Notice the similarities between the definitions of the words with the same root.

43

© 2004 Walch Publishing

Defining Derived Words III

In each sentence below, a root is in bold. Look up the root to find its meaning. Then figure out what the entire word means. Write the definition for the word, underlining the definition of the root. You may want to use a dictionary.

Example: It is **evid**ent that he is lying. **Definition**: easy to <u>see</u>

1. In schools of earlier times, reading was taught by the **phon**ics method.

   Definition:

2. Although she began her career as a **botan**ist, she became a politician.

   Definition:

3. Navigators in early days used an **astro**labe to determine their positions.

   Definition:

44

List more examples of words with these roots in the space below. If you do not know the definitions of your examples, look them up in the dictionary. Notice the similarities between the definitions of the words with the same root.

© 2004 Walch Publishing

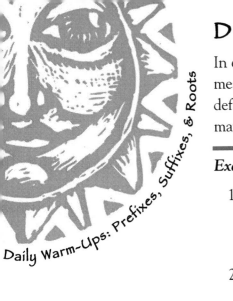

Defining Derived Words IV

In each sentence below, a root is in bold. Look up the root to find its meaning. Then figure out what the entire word means. Write the definition for the word, underlining the definition of the root. You may want to use a dictionary for the more difficult words.

Example: It is **evid**ent that he is lying. **Definition:** easy to <u>see</u>

1. He is a rather intro**spect**ive person who seldom participates in group activities.

   Definition:

2. The **dict**um of the council was that the punishment should be carried out.

   Definition:

List more examples of words with these roots in the space below. If you do not know the definitions of your examples, look them up in the dictionary. Notice the similarities between the definitions of the words with the same root.

45

Defining Derived Words V

In each sentence below, a root is in bold. Look up the root to find its meaning. Then figure out what the entire word means. Write the definition for the word, underlining the definition of the root. You may want to use a dictionary.

Example: It is ev**id**ent that he is lying. **Definition:** easy to <u>see</u>

1. I am glad I do not live in the Mes**azo**ic era.

   Definition:

2. The sunflower is a **photo**tropic plant.

   Definition:

List more examples of words with these roots in the space below. If you do not know the definitions of your examples, look them up in the dictionary. Notice the similarities between the definitions of the words with the same root.

Defining Derived Words VI

In each sentence below, a root is in bold. Look up the root to find its meaning. Then figure out what the entire word means. Write the definition for the word, underlining the definition of the root. You may want to use a dictionary for the more difficult words.

Example: It is ev**id**ent that he is lying. ***Definition:*** easy to <u>see</u>

1. That politician is nothing but a **dem**agogue.

   Definition:

2. Her path to success was **tort**uous.

   Definition:

List more examples of words with these roots in the space below. If you do not know the definitions of your examples, look them up in the dictionary. Notice the similarities between the definitions of the words with the same root.

47

Using Derived Words 1

Write a brief definition of each lettered word. Then match each word with the best sentence by writing its letter in the line to the left of the sentence.

a. chromosphere _____

b. pacifists _____

c. Archeozoic _____

d. dermatologist _____

_____ 1. A group of _____ demonstrated against the war.

_____ 2. Because of my acne, the doctor sent me to a(n) _____.

_____ 3. The _____ is a bright-colored layer of gas around the sun.

_____ 4. The _____ era was the time two billion years ago when simple one-celled animals first appeared on the earth.

48

Using Derived Words II

Write a brief definition of each lettered word. Then match each word with the best sentence by writing its letter in the line to the left of the sentence.

a. chronicle _____

b. incredulous _____

c. democracy _____

d. congregate_____

_____ 1. I think I shall write a(n) _____ of my life, with the dates of all the major events.

_____ 2. Every afternoon the students _____ at the malt shop.

_____ 3. I was _____ that she missed the party, since she had been talking about it for weeks.

_____ 4. Abe Lincoln said that a _____ was a government "of the people, by the people, and for the people."

49

Using Derived Words III

Write a brief definition of each lettered word. Then match each word with the best sentence by writing its letter in the line to the left of the sentence.

a. fidelity _____

b. novitiate _____

c. pyre _____

d. geocentric _____

_____ 1. Because of their _____ to the members of their family, dogs are regarded as family.

_____ 2. In India, they used to practice the custom of *suttee*, in which a widow cast herself on her husband's funeral _____ and allowed herself to be burned to death along with his body.

_____ 3. He spend some time as a _____ in a Buddhist monastery.

_____ 4. The _____ theory of the universe was disproved, and now we believe in the heliocentric model.

More Roots I

The numbered items below are roots and their meanings. The lettered items are incomplete words and their definitions. Match the correct root and word by filling in the lines with the missing root.

1. arch   first, chief

2. anthrop   man, human

3. aud   hear

4. cess, cede, ceed   move

5. clar   clear

a. _____ify—to make clear

b. _____ology—the study of humans and their cultures

c. in_____ible—cannot be heard

d. mon_____—ruler

e. pro_____ion—a group in motion, a parade

Now write a sentence using at least two of your completed words.

© 2004 Walch Publishing

More Roots II

The numbered items below are roots and their meanings. The lettered items are incomplete words and their definitions. Match the correct root and word by filling in the lines with the missing root.

1. graph   write

2. hemo   blood

3. laud   praise

4. leg   law

5. lith   stone

a. tele_____—an instrument for sending messages at a distance

b. _____islature—a group of lawmakers

c. _____ograph—a print made from a plain stone or metal plate

d. app_____—to clap one's hands

e. _____globin—an ingredient in blood

Now write a sentence using at least two of your completed words.

More Roots III

The numbered items below are roots and their meanings. The lettered items are incomplete words and their definitions. Match the correct root and word by filling in the lines with the missing root.

1. log, logue   speech, word

2. pend   hang

3. pos, pon   place, put

4. sen   old

5. sci   know

a. _____ant—an ornament that hangs around the neck

b. de_____it—to store in a bank for safekeeping

c. _____ence—a branch of study

d. _____ior—an older person; one in the last year of high school or college

e. mono_____—a speech by one person

Now write a sentence using at least two of your completed words.

53

More Roots IV

The numbered items below are roots and their meanings. The lettered items are incomplete words and their definitions. Match the correct root and word by filling in the lines with the missing root.

1. sta   stand firm, steady

2. struct   build

3. tect   cover

4. ten   hold

5. thermo   heat

a. recon_____—to rebuild

b. _____tionary—not moving

c. _____acious—not giving up

d. de_____—to discover

e. _____stat—a device for regulating temperature

Now write a sentence using at least two of your completed words.

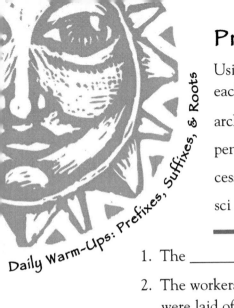

Practice with Additional Roots 1

Using the list of roots below, fill in the incomplete words in each sentence. You will not use all the roots.

arch	graph	leg	laud	clar
pend	struct	aud	ten	hemo
cess	keg	sen	anthrop	tect
sci	thermo	sta	pos	lith

1. The _____bishop gave a speech in the _____itorium.

2. The workers with the most _____iority kept their jobs, but others were laid off during the re_____ion.

3. In con_____ing a new house, it is a good idea to install _____pane windows.

4. It would be easier to know whether something is _____al if our laws were written with greater _____ity.

5. Ships have _____bilizing devices and various instruments to determine their exact _____itions at sea.

55

Practice with Additional Roots II

Using the list of roots below, fill in the incomplete words in each sentence. You will not use all the roots.

arch	graph	log	laud	clar
pend	struct	aud	ten	hemo
cess	keg	sen	anthrop	tect
sci	thermo	sta	pos	lith

1. Whether that _____ant can meet her payments de_____s on the price she gets for her crops.

2. An uncon_____ous person cannot engage in dia_____ue.

3. They did a _____able job in building that monument of grano_____.

4. _____oid apes walk partly on their hind legs, make simple tools, pro_____ their young in various ways, and perform other interesting activities.

5. The cardio_____ showed nothing abnormal, but other tests revealed a _____toma.

56

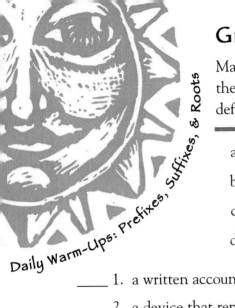

Graph 1

Match the following words with the root *graph* (meaning *write*) with their definitions. Write the letter of the word in the line next to its definition.

a. biography   e. lithograph   i. photograph

b. cartography   f. monograph   j. stenographer

c. graphite   g. oceanography   k. telegraph

d. graphologist   h. phonograph

_____ 1. a written account of a single topic

_____ 2. a device that reproduces sound by using discs with grooves in them

_____ 3. a picture taken with a camera

_____ 4. a device for communicating at a distance using dot and dash signals

_____ 5. a book about the life of a person

Think of some other words that contain the root *graph*, and list them below.

57

Graph II

Match the following words with the root *graph* (meaning *write*) with their definitions. Write the letter of the word in the line next to its definition.

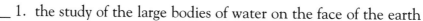

a. biography

b. cartography

c. graphite

d. graphologist

e. lithograph

f. monograph

g. oceanography

h. phonograph

i. photograph

j. stenographer

k. telegraph

____ 1. the study of the large bodies of water on the face of the earth

____ 2. mapmaking

____ 3. a soft carbon used in pencils

____ 4. one who studies handwriting to analyze a writer's character

____ 5. one who takes diction in shorthand

____ 6. a print made from a plain stone or metal plate

Write a sentence using three of the words in the exercise above.

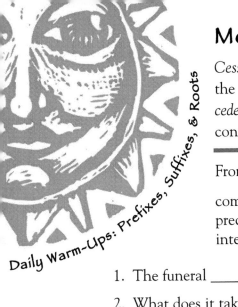

Motion 1

Cess, ceed, cede, mov, and *mot* are roots that refer to motion. Some of the words made from these roots are tricky to spell because the roots *cede, ceed,* and *sede* have the same sound (for example: proceed, concede, supersede).

From the list below, select the roots that fit into the sentences.

commotion	motivate	movie	recede	predecessor
precede	successor	exceed	movable	motive
intercede	movement	procession	concede	supersede

1. The funeral _____ moved slowly down Main Street. (gathering)

2. What does it take to _____ him to do his homework? (stimulate)

3. The flood waters have started to _____. (diminish)

4. John Kennedy's _____ was Lyndon Johnson. (one who follows)

5. These new rules _____ those issued in 1983. (take place of)

59

© 2004 Walch Publishing

Motion II

Cess, *ceed*, *cede*, *mov*, and *mot* are roots that refer to motion. Some of the words made from these roots are tricky to spell because the roots *cede*, *ceed*, and *sede* have the same sound (for example: proceed, concede, supersede).

From the list below, select the roots that fit into the sentences.

commotion	motivate	movie	recede	predecessor
precede	successor	exceed	movable	motive
intercede	movement	procession	concede	supersede

1. What is the _____ for the crime? (the reason behind it)

2. I refuse to _____. (to yield)

3. There has been a recent downward _____ in the stock market. (shift)

4. I wish someone could _____ and stop the feud. (step in between two parties)

5. This heavy piano is barely _____.

6. When the announcement was made, there was a great _____ in the audience. (noise, confusion)

60

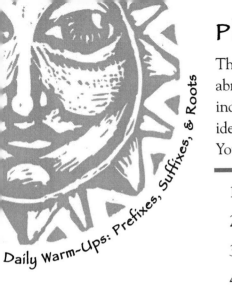

Phobias I

The root *phobia* comes from a word meaning *fear*. It refers to an abnormal type of fear. Other roots and prefixes added to this root indicate the type of fear. How many of the following phobias can you identify? Write the missing word in each definition line indicated. You may need a dictionary for help.

1. algophobia   fear of __ __ __ __
2. thanatophobia   fear of __ __ __ __ __
3. zoophobia   fear of __ __ __ __ __ __ __
4. lalophobia   fear of __ __ __ __ __ __ __ __

Have you heard of the word *panphobia*? Using a dictionary, write the definition of this word in the space below. Then, create a complete sentence using this word.

61

Phobias II

The root *phobia* comes from a word meaning *fear*. It refers to an abnormal type of fear. Other roots and prefixes added to this root indicate the type of fear. How many of the following phobias can you identify? Write the missing word on the definition lines indicated. You may need a dictionary for help.

1. acrophobia   fear of __ __ __ __ __ __ __

2. hemophobia   fear of __ __ __ __ __ __

3. toxicophobia   fear of __ __ __ __ __ __ __

4. hydrophobia   fear of __ __ __ __ __ __

Can you think of other phobias? Write some phobias and their definitions below.

62

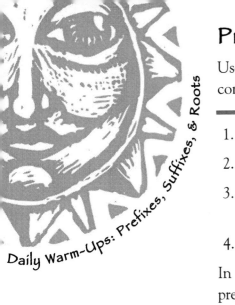

Prefixes: With, Together

Use the prefixes *con-*, *com-*, and *cor-* (meaning *with*, *together*) to complete the words and make sensible sentences.

1. The numbers on this map _____respond with those on the chart.

2. To end a dispute, sometimes both sides must _____promise.

3. The parents on our block held a _____ference to discuss the possibility of establishing a neighborhood playground.

4. A poor diet _____tributed to his illness.

In the space below, write other examples of words that contain these prefixes.

63

©2004 Walch Publishing

Prefixes: Toward

The prefix *ad-* means *to* or *toward*. Read the sentences below and write the word that best completes the sentence. Then write a definition of each *ad-* word that includes the prefix meaning.

adapt   admit   adhere

1. When you use this glue, metal will _____ to the wood.

   Definition:

2. When I moved from Florida to Maine it was difficult to _____ to the cold weather.

   Definition:

3. The prisoner refused to _____ his part in the crime.

   Definition:

64

The prefix *ad-* changes spelling when it is attached to roots that start with certain letters. For example, it changes to *as-* before words starting with *s*, such as assemble. It changes to *af-* before words starting with *f*, such as affix. List other examples below.

Prefixes: Away, Apart

Use the prefixes *de-* (from, down, away) and *di-* or *dis-* (apart) to complete the words and make sensible sentences.

1. Don't try to _____vert my attention, because I must get this done.

2. Sometimes illegal aliens are _____ported.

3. Most of the oranges we bought in California were _____cayed by the time we got home.

4. Pleasant music helps to _____pel loneliness.

In the space below, write other examples of words that contain these prefixes.

65

Prefixes: Through, Back

Use the prefixes *per-* (through) and *re-* (back, again) to complete the words and make sensible sentences.

1. I cannot give you _____mission to go.

2. This _____fume has a floral scent, and that one has a spicy fragrance.

3. The case was _____opened after new evidence was found.

4. I forgot to spray myself with insect _____pellent before I went fishing.

In the space below, write other examples of words that contain these prefixes.

66

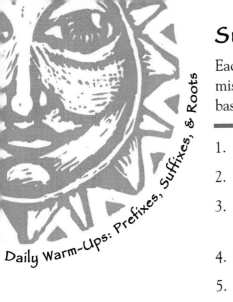

Supplying Prefixes 1

Each sentence defines the word missing its prefix. The meaning of the missing prefix is underlined in the definition. Fill in the correct prefix based on these clues.

1. A talk by <u>one</u> person is a _____logue.

2. When you walk <u>around</u>, you _____ambulate.

3. An animal that has <u>four</u> legs, such as a horse or a cow, is a _____ruped.

4. Something <u>under</u> the earth is _____terranean.

5. If something has <u>no</u> harmony, it is said to be _____harmonious.

6. Buses running <u>inside</u> a city are called _____-urban buses, while those running between cities are inter-urban buses.

67

Supplying Prefixes II

Each sentence defines the word missing its prefix. The meaning of the missing prefix is underlined in the definition. Fill in the correct prefix based on these clues.

1. When you are spying <u>against</u> other spies, you are involved in _____ espionage.

2. A figure with <u>many</u> sides is a _____ gon.

3. Half a circle is a _____ circle.

4. An instrument for cutting <u>very small</u> items is a _____ tome.

5. A hat with <u>three</u> sides (such as those worn in Colonial days) is a _____ corn.

6. To <u>forecast</u> what will happen is to _____ dict.

7. To pay someone <u>back</u> is to _____ compense.

68

Supplying Prefixes III

Each sentence defines the word missing its prefix. The meaning of the missing prefix is underlined in the definition. Fill in the correct prefix based on these clues.

1. The measurement of things from <u>far</u> away is _____metry.

2. A(n) _____national agreement is one made <u>among</u> many different nations.

3. A book about one's life written by one<u>self</u> is an _____biography.

4. When you get into a predicament, you must find a way to _____tricate yourself <u>from</u> it.

5. Someone who is <u>above</u> you in rank is your _____ior.

6. The period of history <u>before</u> the Civil War is known as the _____bellum period.

7. Something from <u>beyond</u> the earth is _____terrestrial.

69

Supplying Prefixes IV

Match each prefix on the left with a word on the right. Write the prefixes on the lines provided. Then use each word in a sentence that also contains the meaning of the prefix.

re-

in-

dis-

over-

fore-

1. _____honest

2. _____tread

3. _____reacted

4. _____finger

5. _____correct

70

Supplying Prefixes V

Match each prefix on the left with a word on the right. Write the prefixes on the lines provided. Then use each word in a sentence that also contains the meaning of the prefix.

trans-

post-

mid-

pre-

in-

1. _____day

2. _____graduate

3. _____determined

4. _____atlantic

5. _____conspicuous

71

Supplying Prefixes VI

Match each prefix on the left with a word on the right. Write the prefixes on the lines provided. Then use each word in a sentence that also contains the meaning of the prefix.

post-

trans-

mid-

re-

dis-

1. _____obey

2. _____script

3. _____air

4. _____continental

5. _____fuel

72

Supplying Prefixes VII

Match each prefix on the left with a word on the right. Write the prefixes on the lines provided. Then use each word in a sentence that also contains the meaning of the prefix.

fore-

over-

pre-

post-

dis-

1. _____slept

2. _____dominant

3. _____agree

4. _____word

5. _____mortem

73

Supplying Prefixes VIII

Match each prefix on the left with a word on the right. Write the prefixes on the lines provided. Then use each word in a sentence that also contains the meaning of the prefix.

in-

re-

over-

fore-

mid-

1. _____ground

2. _____point

3. _____effective

4. _____discover

5. _____time

Supplying Prefixes IX

Supply the missing prefix in each word below. The meaning of the root is underlined in each definition.

1. _____cavate—to dig <u>out</u> a hollow area, as for a house foundation

2. _____sensory—<u>beyond</u> the five senses

3. _____librium—in balance, as when both sides of a scale are <u>equal</u>

4. _____photo lens—a camera lens for shooting things <u>far</u> away

5. _____-Siberian Railway—a track laid <u>across</u> Siberia

Choose two words used in the above exercise and write two complete sentences for each in the space below.

75

© 2004 Walch Publishing

Supplying Prefixes X

Supply the missing prefix in each word below. The meaning of the root is underlined in each definition.

1. _____lateral—having <u>three</u> sides

2. _____sede—to go <u>over</u> something else, to take its place

3. _____ordinate clause—a group of words that is of less importance than another clause in the sentence; it is <u>under</u> the other clause in rank

4. _____annual—occurring every <u>half</u> year.

5. _____monish—to give a warning <u>to</u>; to scold

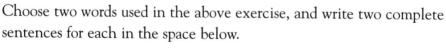

Choose two words used in the above exercise, and write two complete sentences for each in the space below.

76

Supplying Prefixes XI

Supply the missing prefix in each word below. The meaning of the root is underlined in each definition.

1. _____aircraft weapons—weapons used in defense <u>against</u> enemy aircraft

2. _____nomous—<u>self</u>-governing

3. _____aria—a disease originally believed to be cause by <u>bad</u> air

4. _____demeanor—a <u>wrong</u> deed; a breaking of the law

5. _____rib—the <u>middle</u> vein in a leaf

Choose two words used in the above exercise, and write two complete sentences for each in the space below.

77

Numerical Prefixes I

Using what you know about prefixes, draw pictures for each word below that clearly illustrates its definition. Use your dictionary, if necessary.

1. bicuspid

3. trident

2. octopus

4. quadrilateral

What other words can you think of that contain these prefixes? List them below.

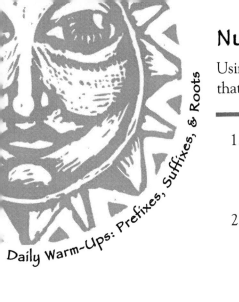

Numerical Prefixes II

Using what you know about prefixes, draw pictures for each word below that clearly illustrates its definition. Use your dictionary, if necessary.

1. quintuplets

2. unicorn

3. octagon

4. hexagram

What other words can you think of that contain these prefixes? List them below.

79

Numerical Prefixes III

Write the definitions for each of the following words, all of which have numerical prefixes. You may use a dictionary, if necessary.

1. bicep: _____

2. centavo: _____

3. decathlon: _____

4. duplex: _____

5. millipede: _____

In the space below, write three sentences, each with at least one word from the above list.

80

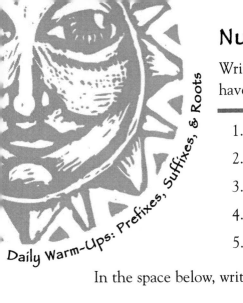

Numerical Prefixes IV

Write the definitions for each of the following words, all of which have numerical prefixes. You may use a dictionary, if necessary.

1. monochromatic: _____

2. octodont: _____

3. septennial: _____

4. sexagenarian: _____

5. trefoil: _____

In the space below, write three sentences, each with at least one word from the above list.

81

Numerical Prefixes V

Fill in the numbers missing from the sentences below.

1. A quatrain consists of _____ lines of a poem.

2. A unicycle has _____ wheel.

3. A nonagenarian is a person who has lived for _____ decades.

4. A vocal sextet consists of _____ singers.

5. An actor who plays _____ parts is said to have a dual role.

6. A heptagon has _____ sides.

7. The Pentagon in Washington, D.C., is a _____-sided building.

8. A triarchy or a triumvirate is a form of government headed by _____ persons.

9. A musical octave consists of _____ notes.

82

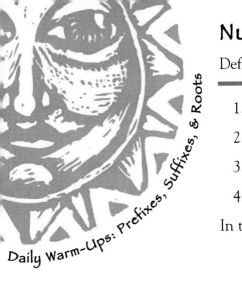

Numerical Prefixes VI

Define the following words, which all have the same numerical prefix.

1. decagon: _____

2. decalogue: _____

3. decameter: _____

4. decapod: _____

In the space below, write a sentence for each of the words listed above.

83

Sub- 1

The Latin prefix *sub-* means *under* or *below*. This is its basic meaning. Several other meanings have developed from the basic meaning. Five meanings of *sub-* are listed below.

a. under or below

b. part of

c. of lower rank than, less important than

d. slightly, somewhat

e. near, next to but not necessarily beneath

For each sentence, decide which meaning best completes the definition. Write the letter of the definition on the line.

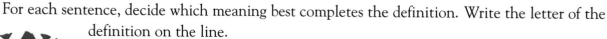

1. A submarine travels ___ water.

2. A sublieutenant in the British Army is ___ than a lieutenant.

3. A subarid region is ___ dry, but it is not as dry as a desert.

4. The subsoil is a layer of earth ___ the surface.

5. An orange is a subacid fruit. This means it is ___ acid.

6. Something that is substandard is ___ the normal condition.

7. The subarctic region lies ___ the Arctic region.

Sub- II

The Latin prefix *sub-* means *under* or *below*. This is its basic meaning. Several other meanings have developed from the basic meaning. Five meanings of *sub-* are listed below.

a. under or below

b. part of

c. of lower rank than, less important than

d. slightly, somewhat

e. near, next to but not necessarily beneath

For each sentence, decide which meaning best completes the definition. Write the letter of the definition on the line.

1. A subtreasury is a branch of or ___ the U.S. Treasury.

2. In arithmetic, the subtrahend is the number you place ___ the minuend in order to subtract.

3. A subtopic is ___ the main topic.

4. The subagent is ___ the agent who assigns duties to him or her.

5. When you submerge something, you put it ___ water.

85

Super-, Hyper-, Extra- 1

Super-, *hyper-*, and *extra-* all mean *above, over, beyond,* or *higher*. Select one of these three prefixes to complete each of the words in the sentences below. If you are not sure which prefix to use, check the word in the dictionary.

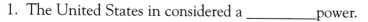

1. The United States in considered a _____ power.

2. She is _____ critical of everyone around her.

3. What _____ curricular activities, besides band, do you participate in?

4. The term _____ tension refers to the condition accompanying high blood pressure.

5. John Edwards claims to have _____ natural powers since he can forecast future events.

6. Wasn't that the most _____ ordinary performance you have ever seen?

7. Any creature not from earth would be called an _____ terrestrial being.

86

Super-, Hyper-, Extra- II

Super-, *hyper-*, and *extra-* all mean *above, over, beyond,* or *higher*. Select one of these three prefixes to complete each of the words in the sentences below. If you are not sure which prefix to use, check the word in the dictionary.

1. The extra trimming is _____fluous.

2. Taking too many deep breaths causes loss of carbon dioxide from the blood. This is referred to as _____ventilation.

3. Some people claim to have _____sensory perception.

4. The parts of a ship above the deck are called the _____structure.

5. _____opia is far-sightedness.

6. An excess of sugar in the blood is referred to as _____glycemia.

7. Buying more than one new hat for Easter is an _____vagance.

8. When she rescued three people from the capsized boat, she displayed _____human physical effort.

87

Adverb and Verb Prefixes I

Prefixes that are often found in verbs include *be-* as in *bewitch*, *de-* as in *degrade*, *em-* as in *empower*, *en-* as in *endear*, *re-* as in *recover*, and *with-* as in *withstand*. In the couplets below, supply a rhyming verb that contains one of these prefixes.

1. The policeman said, "Here you cannot park your horse.

   Sorry, the law I must __ __ f o __ __ __."

2. I drank the soda intended for Jill;

   So now her glass I must __ __ f i __ __.

3. Your happiness will have no end,

   If those in need you will __ __ f r __ __ __ __.

88

Now, using the verb *recover*, make up your own rhyme in the space below.

Adverb and Verb Prefixes II

Prefixes that are often found in verbs include *be-* as in *bewitch*, *de-* as in *degrade*, *em-* as in *empower*, *en-* as in *endear*, *re-* as in *recover*, and *with-* as in *withstand*. In the couplets below, supply a rhyming verb that contains one of these prefixes.

1. You won't be trapped in a liar's snare,

   If the truth you always __ __ c l __ __ __.

2. In order to buy a gift for Maw,

   From my bank account I must __ __ __ __ d r __ __.

3. Let's walk out to the lake in the park,

   And then on my boat we will __ __ b a __ __.

Now, using the verb *bewitch*, make up your own rhyme in the space below.

89

© 2004 Walch Publishing

Adverb Prefixes

The prefix *a-* is found on a number of adverbs. Examples are *away*, *around*, and *apart*.

Using a dictionary, see how many adverbs you can find with this prefix. Then, write five sentences, each with at least one of the adverbs you find.

90

Spelling Derived Words I

When you attach a prefix to a word, do not change the spelling of the word or add or subtract letters. For example, when you add *dis-* to *interested*, you merely connect the two (*disinterested*). When you attach *dis-* to *similar*, you make no changes (*dissimilar*), even though the combination has a double *s*. The prefixes *mis-*, *un-*, *under-*, *over-*, and *in-* follow the same rule, as do the variations of *in-*, including *im-*, *il-*, and *ir-*.

In the list of words below, change the spelling of the words you think are spelled incorrectly. In addition, write a brief definition of each word.

1. disappoint
2. immobilize
3. misfortune
4. irreversible
5. overrated
6. dissagree
7. disease
8. misstake

91

© 2004 Walch Publishing

Spelling Derived Words II

When you attach a prefix to a word, do not change the spelling of the word or add or subtract letters. For example, when you add *dis-* to *interested*, you merely connect the two (*disinterested*). When you attach *dis-* to *similar*, you make no changes (*dissimilar*), even though the combination has a double *s*. The prefixes *mis-*, *un-*, *under-*, *over-*, and *in-* follow the same rule, as do the variations of *in-*, including *im-*, *il-*, and *ir-*.

In the list of words below, change the spelling of the words you think are spelled incorrectly. In addition, write a brief definition of each word.

1. illuminate

2. misstep

3. misrepresent

4. irresponsible

5. ilegal

6. disolve

7. disunity

8. disappear

Spelling Derived Words III

When you attach a prefix to a word, do not change the spelling of the word or add or subtract letters. For example, when you add *dis-* to *interested*, you merely connect the two (*disinterested*). When you attach *dis-* to *similar*, you make no changes (*dissimilar*), even though the combination has a double *s*. The prefixes *mis-*, *un-*, *under-*, *over-*, and *in-* follow the same rule, as do the variations of *in-*, including *im-*, *il-*, and *ir-*.

In the list of words below, change the spelling of the words you think are spelled incorrectly. In addition, write a brief definition of each word.

1. inumerable
2. misbehave
3. iregular
4. illegible
5. unatural
6. mislead
7. override
8. impenetrable

93

Spelling Derived Words IV

When you attach a prefix to a word, do not change the spelling of the word or add or subtract letters. For example, when you add *dis-* to *interested*, you merely connect the two (*disinterested*). When you attach *dis-* to *similar*, you make no changes (*dissimilar*), even though the combination has a double *s*. The prefixes *mis-*, *un-*, *under-*, *over-*, and *in-* follow the same rule, as do the variations of *in-*, including *im-*, *il-*, and *ir-*.

In the list of words below, change the spelling of the words you think are spelled incorrectly. In addition, write a brief definition of each word.

1. imature

2. dissimilar

3. underated

4. illogical

5. irreverent

6. overregulate

7. mispoke

8. immodest

94

Using Hyphens in Prefixes 1

Most prefixes are attached directly to words, but some are hyphenated. The prefix *ex-*, when it means *out of*, is attached. But when it means *former*, it is usually hyphenated (*ex-teacher*). Prefixes before proper nouns are often, but not always, hyphenated.

In each sentence below, one word is missing a prefix. Using the prefix *ex-*, decide whether to write it with or without a hyphen in each sentence. Use a dictionary, if necessary.

1. The international _____position will be held in 2005.

2. An _____soldier, who lost a leg in World War II, spoke to the injured soldiers in the field hospital.

In the space below, list one word with the prefix *ex-* that is hyphenated and one word that is not hyphenated. Try to find an exception to the rule. Briefly define each word, using your dictionary if necessary.

95

© 2004 Walch Publishing

Using Hyphens in Prefixes II

Most prefixes are attached directly to the words, but some are hyphenated. The prefix *self-* is generally hyphenated (*self-conscious*). Prefixes before proper nouns are often, but not always, hyphenated.

In each sentence below, one word is missing a prefix. Using the prefix *self-*, decide whether to write it with or without a hyphen in each sentence. Use a dictionary, if necessary.

1. He is _____ less in his devotion to his wife, who has a physical impairment.

2. The people on this island are largely _____ sufficient, raising their own food, producing their own clothes, and building their own shelters.

   In the space below, list one word with the prefix *self-* that is hyphenated and one word that is not hyphenated. Try to find an exception to the rule. Briefly define each word, using your dictionary if necessary.

96

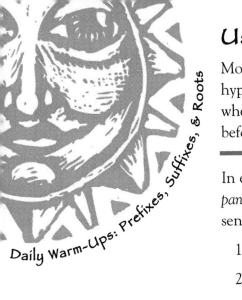

Using Hyphens in Prefixes III

Most prefixes are attached directly to words, but some are hyphenated. The prefix *pan-*, meaning *all*, is generally hyphenated when it refers to an entire group (*Pan-American Union*). Prefixes before proper nouns are often, but not always, hyphenated.

In each sentence below, one word is missing a prefix. Using the prefix *pan-*, decide whether to write it with or without a hyphen in each sentence. Use a dictionary, if necessary.

1. _____chromatic film is sensitive to all colors in the spectrum.

2. There is a great deal of fighting among members of the _____Islamic world.

In the space below, list one word with the prefix *pan-* that is hyphenated and one word that is not hyphenated. Try to find an exception to the rule. Briefly define each word, using your dictionary if necessary.

97

Using Hyphens in Prefixes IV

Most prefixes are attached directly to words, but some are hyphenated. The prefix *non-*, meaning *other than* or *not*, is generally not hyphenated. Prefixes before proper nouns are often, but not always, hyphenated.

In each sentence below, one word is missing a prefix. Using the prefix *non-*, decide whether to write it with or without a hyphen in each sentence. Use a dictionary, if necessary.

1. During the Great Schism, from 1378–1417, there were two popes, one Roman pope and one _____Roman pope.

2. This drug is _____addictive.

In the space below, list one word with the prefix *non-* that is hyphenated and one word that is not hyphenated. Try to find an exception to the rule. Briefly define each word, using your dictionary if necessary.

Using Hyphens in Prefixes V

Most prefixes are attached directly to words, but some are hyphenated. The prefix *co-* is hyphenated sometimes (*co-worker*), but it is usually attached (*copilot*). Some words that were originally hyphenated are no longer hyphenated (*cooperative*), while others may be written both ways (*co-author, coauthor*).

In each sentence below, one word is missing a prefix. Using the prefix *co-*, decide whether to write it with or without a hyphen in each sentence. Use a dictionary, if necessary.

1. Adding vinegar to milk may cause it to _____agulate.

2. These two men are _____agents in this project.

Why do you think *co-worker* is hyphenated and *copilot* is not?

99

© 2004 Walch Publishing

Using Hyphens in Prefixes VI

Most prefixes are attached directly to words, but some are hyphenated. In cases when the prefix *re-* (meaning *again* or *back*) may cause confusion, it is hyphenated. For example, when you use the word *recover* to mean to *cover again*, you must hyphenate it to distinguish it from *recover* meaning *to get well*.

In each sentence below, one word is missing a prefix. Using the prefix *re-*, decide whether to write it with or without a hyphen in each sentence. Use a dictionary, if necessary.

1. I accidentally dropped my clay figure, so I must _____ form it.

2. This whole program needs drastic _____ form.

In the space below, list one word with the prefix *re-* that is hyphenated and one word that is not hyphenated. Try to find an exception to the rule. Briefly define each word, using your dictionary if necessary.

© 2004 Walch Publishing

Adjective Suffixes I

Each adjective in the list below is missing its suffix. Each group of three words requires the same suffix. Add each suffix. Then choose one word from each group, and use it in a sentence.

1. fest__ __ __

2. repuls__ __ __

3. apprehens__ __ __

4. courage__ __ __

5. boister__ __ __

6. ridicul__ __ __

101

© 2004 Walch Publishing

Adjective Suffixes II

Each adjective in the list below is missing its suffix. Each group of three words requires the same suffix. Add each suffix. Then choose one word from each group, and use it in a sentence.

1. reli__ __ __ __

2. charit__ __ __ __

3. ami__ __ __ __

4. fear__ __ __ __

5. ruth__ __ __ __

6. spine__ __ __ __

102

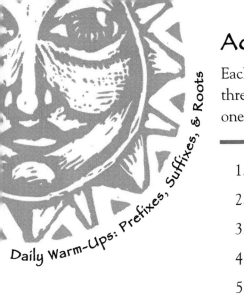

Adjective Suffixes III

Each adjective in the list below is missing its suffix. Each group of three words requires the same suffix. Add each suffix. Then choose one word from each group, and use it in a sentence.

1. grace__ __ __

2. spite__ __ __

3. help__ __ __

4. obstin__ __ __

5. compassion__ __ __

6. fortun__ __ __

103

© 2004 Walch Publishing

Adjective Suffixes IV

Each adjective in the list below is missing its suffix. Each group of
three words requires the same suffix. Add each suffix. Then choose
one word from each group, and use it in a sentence.

1. exot__ __

2. sympathet__ __

3. antagonist__ __

4. fragr__ __ __

5. toler__ __ __

6. exuber__ __ __

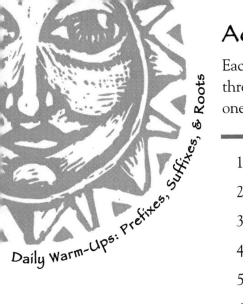

Adjective Suffixes V

Each adjective in the list below is missing its suffix. Each group of three words requires the same suffix. Add each suffix. Then choose one word from each group, and use it in a sentence.

1. fool__ __ __

2. purpl__ __ __

3. Turk__ __ __

4. tradition__ __

5. topic__ __

6. fiction__ __

105

Verb Suffixes I

Add a suffix to each of the incomplete verbs below so that each sentence makes sense.

1. This mask may fright__ __ the children.

2. All students should familiar__ __ __ themselves with these formulas.

3. Trees beaut__ __ __ a piece of property.

4. I knew he was up to no good when I saw his eyes twink__ __.

5. Scientists often general__ __ __ a conclusion from a specific observation.

Write at least one example of a different word for each suffix in the exercises above.

106

Verb Suffixes II

Add a suffix to each of the incomplete verbs below so that each sentence makes sense.

1. We will just have to fabric__ __ __ something from the materials on hand.

2. This damp piece of wood might buck__ __ when it dries out.

3. Your pain will less__ __ after a few hours.

4. This magician can really myst__ __ __ the audience.

5. The negotiators are trying to liber__ __ __ the political prisoners.

Write at least one example of a different word for each suffix in the exercises above.

107

© 2004 Walch Publishing

Verb Suffixes III

Add a suffix to each of the incomplete verbs below so that each sentence makes sense.

1. It is better to praise something done well than to critic__ __ __ something done poorly.

2. How can you just__ __ __ your actions in this matter?

3. Let's formul__ __ __ a new plan now that we have more facts.

4. The guerillas constantly terror__ __ __ the villagers.

5. My mom uses reading glasses to magni__ __ the words on the page.

Write at least one example of a different word for each suffix in the exercises above.

108

Noun Suffixes 1

Read the sentences below, and find a noun suffix in each one. Write the suffix on the line at the left.

_____ 1. His loyalty has never been questioned previously.

_____ 2. Please print a duplicate of this form for Mrs. Anderson.

_____ 3. The balloonist descended as the crowd watched.

_____ 4. The operator instructed me to dial again later.

_____ 5. Did you decide to apply for a four-year scholarship?

_____ 6. Ever since childhood, he has wanted to play the violin.

_____ 7. Everyone was shocked at his mysterious reappearance.

109

Noun Suffixes II

Read the sentences below, and find a noun suffix in each one. Write the suffix on the line at the left.

_____ 1. Sarah is studying journalism, and her sister is preparing to become a lawyer.

_____ 2. Her stubbornness is bound to get her into trouble sooner or later.

_____ 3. My assistant made a serious mistake.

_____ 4. The nurse reported that his condition was stable but still not normal.

_____ 5. The media gave the event considerable coverage.

_____ 6. Because he continued misbehaving, he was given a three-day suspension.

_____ 7. This draftee has to report for service on Monday next week.

Spelling Adverb Suffixes 1

The suffix *-ly* is most often used in forming adverbs. Generally, the suffix *-ly* is added without changing the spelling of the root word. For example, if the word ends in *l*, adding *-ly* will result in a double *l* (*naturally*).

However, when a word ends in *c*, you usually add the letters *al* before adding *-ly*, as when you change *automatic* to *automatically*.

Keeping these rules in mind, change each word below into an adverb ending in *-ly*.

1. electric: _____

2. formal: _____

3. nice: _____

4. frantic: _____

5. magic: _____

6. free: _____

7. beautiful: _____

Write more examples of words that end in *-ly* in the space below.

111

Spelling Adverb Suffixes II

The suffix *-y* is most often used in forming adverbs. Generally, the suffix *-ly* is added without changing the spelling of the root word. For example, if the word ends in *l*, adding *-ly* will result in a double *l* (*naturally*).

However, when a word ends in *c*, you usually add the letters *al* before adding *-ly*, as when you change *automatic* to *automatically*.

There is one word in the list below that is spelled correctly, even though it doesn't follow the rule for *-ly* suffixes. Circle the correctly spelled word, and correct the rest of the words. You may use your dictionary.

1. tenderlly

2. energeticly

3. electricaly

4. gradualy

5. confidentialy

6. artisticaly

7. publicly

Practicing with Suffixes 1

Add suffixes to the words below to form the correct word for the
definition on the right.

1. novel__ __ __   one who writes novels

   novel__ __   something new and different

2. help__ __ __   giving help

   help__ __ __ __   without help

3. employ__ __   one who works for someone else

   employ__ __   a boss, one who hires others

4. kind__ __ __ __   the quality of being kind

   kind__ __   in a kind way

In the space below, identify the part of speech formed when each
suffix was added to the root words used above. Some of the words
may be more than one part of speech.

113

Practicing with Suffixes II

Add suffixes to the words below to form the correct word for the definition on the right.

1. atten__ __ __ __   the act of observing carefully

   atten__ __ __ __   courteous, polite

2. termin__ __ __   to end

   termin__ __   at the end; causing the end

3. memor__ __ __   to learn by heart

   memor__   the ability to remember

4. depend__ __ __ __   capable of being depended upon

   depend__ __ __   relying on someone else

114

In the space below, identify the part of speech formed when each suffix was added to the root words used above. Some of the words may be more than one part of speech.

Practicing with Suffixes III

How many suffixes can you add to the root *dent*, meaning *tooth*? List and define your words in the space below.

Look up the word *edentuolous* in a dictionary, and define it in your own words.

115

Practicing with Suffixes IV

From the list of suffixes, select one for each of the words below.
Choose the suffix that best fits the word listed.

-ly	-ist	-ward
-ship	-ous	-er

1. courage_____

2. sky_____

3. champion_____

4. sing_____

5. knowing_____

6. motor_____

116

Choose one of the suffixes used above, and write at least ten more
words with this suffix. Be sure to spell them all correctly. What parts
of speech are the words you have listed?

Practicing with Suffixes V

From the list of suffixes, select one for each of the words below. Choose the suffix that best fits the word listed.

-ly	-ist	-ward
-ship	-ous	-er

1. farm_____

2. home_____

3. ideal_____

4. workman_____

5. unlike_____

6. clamor_____

Choose one of the suffixes used above, and write at least ten more words with this suffix. Be sure to spell them all correctly. What parts of speech are the words you have listed?

117

Practicing with Suffixes VI

From the list of suffixes, select one for each of the words below.
Choose the suffix that best fits the word listed.

-ly   -ist   -ward

-ship   -ous   -er

---

1. west_____

2. violin_____

3. danger_____

4. eventual_____

5. teach_____

6. friend_____

Choose one of the suffixes used above, and write at least ten more
words with this suffix. Be sure to spell them all correctly. What parts
of speech are the words you have listed?

118

Practicing with Suffixes VII

From the list of suffixes, select one for each of the words below. Choose the suffix that best fits the word listed.

-ly	-ist	-ward
-ship	-ous	-er

1. hard_____

2. sea_____

3. poison_____

4. immediate_____

5. reception_____

6. design_____

Choose one of the suffixes used above, and write at least ten more words with this suffix. Be sure to spell them all correctly. What parts of speech are the words you have listed?

119

Practicing with Suffixes VIII

Study the words with the underlined suffixes in each of the sentences below. Decide whether each word is used as a **noun** (names something), a **verb** (shows action, tells what the noun does), an **adjective** (describes a noun), or **adverb** (describes a verb).

1. It took Erica six years in show business to achieve star<u>dom</u>.

2. We can light<u>en</u> the load by removing the heaviest objects.

3. She took charge of the situation very skillful<u>ly</u>.

4. Let's head home<u>ward</u> without delay.

5. Wood<u>en</u> ladders break more easily than aluminum ones.

6. That is quite an imaginat<u>ive</u> plan!

7. Isn't that baby ador<u>able</u>?

8. He has a lot of music<u>al</u> ability.

Look up the word *suffix* in the dictionary to find out its Latin origin. Explain the origin below.

120

Practicing with Suffixes IX

Study the words with the underlined suffixes in each of the sentences below. Decide whether each word is used as a **noun** (names something), a **verb** (shows action, tells what the noun does), an **adjective** (describes a noun), or **adverb** (describes a verb).

1. The North Star shines with great brilli<u>ance</u>.

2. The workers in this factory are hoping to union<u>ize</u>.

3. Did she fals<u>ify</u> her statement?

4. I am not a very good stud<u>ent</u>.

5. He reacted rather violent<u>ly</u>.

6. With that kind of charm, she is sure to captiv<u>ate</u> any audience.

7. Some mattresses have more firm<u>ness</u> than others.

8. I think it's easier to deal cards clock<u>wise</u>.

121

© 2004 Walch Publishing

Practicing with Suffixes X

Form nouns by adding the appropriate suffix to the incomplete word in each sentence below.

1. In this last shipment of dishes, there was minimal break__ __ __.

2. He has a poor record of attend__ __ __ __.

3. We should value our free__ __ __ and do our best to protect it.

4. We had only one absent__ __ from our class today.

5. The wait__ __ gave us great service.

6. Some day Puerto Rico may attain state__ __ __ __, just as Alaska and Hawaii have.

7. His action was not appropriate in that situa__ __ __ __.

8. Hindu__ __ __ is practiced by many people in India.

9. Which cycl__ __ __ won the race?

10. The wedding ceremony was marked by great solemn__ __ __.

122

Practicing with Suffixes XI

In the sentences below, form adjectives by adding appropriate suffixes to the incomplete words.

1. This chair is so heavy that it is barely mov__ __ __ __.

2. This matter is not only of local concern, but also of nation__ __ interest.

3. Mary is skill__ __ __ at weaving baskets.

4. Rover keeps whining and walking around. I wonder what is making him so rest__ __ __ __.

5. When she is asleep, the baby has such an angel__ __ look.

6. I thought the choreography was what made the musical marvel__ __ __.

7. That was a very fool__ __ __ thing to do.

In the sentences below, form verbs by adding appropriate suffixes to the incomplete words.

8. He always tried to domin__ __ __ the conversation.

9. Moist__ __ the back of this sticker, and put it on this corner.

10. You can pur__ __ __ water by passing it through filters.

123

Practicing with Suffixes XII

Complete the words below using the list of suffixes provided. Make sure the new word matches the definition to the right.

-ly	-ship	-ic	-ize	-ist
-ism	-less	-ive	-ful	-age
-ible	-ness	-ance	-tion	-ous
-al	-ian	-ity	-er	-able

124

1. hypnot__ __ __—one who puts people into a trance

2. hypnot__ __ __—to put into a trance

3. hypnot__ __—having a trancelike effect

4. friend__ __ __ __—state of being friends

5. friend__ __—kind, like a friend

6. friend__ __ __ __—without friends

Think of other suffixes that can be added to the roots listed above. Write your answers in the space below.

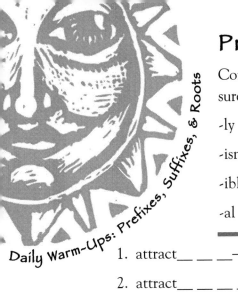

Practicing with Suffixes XIII

Complete the words below using the list of suffixes provided. Make sure the new word matches the definition to the right.

-ly	-ship	-ic	-ize	-ist
-ism	-less	-ive	-ful	-age
-ible	-ness	-ance	-tion	-ous
-al	-ian	-ity	-er	-able

1. attract__ __ __—pretty, pleasing

2. attract__ __ __ __—attractive quality

3. lov__ __ __ __—capable of being loved

4. lov__ __—one who loves

5. electric__ __ __—form of energy that produces light and heat

6. electric__ __ __—a person who installs or repairs electric items

Think of other suffixes that can be added to the roots listed above. Write your answers in the space below.

125

Choosing the Correct Suffix 1

The suffixes *-able* and *-ible* change other parts of speech into adjectives and add the meaning *capable of* or *worthy of*, as in *breakable* (capable of breaking) and *lovable* (worthy of love). It can be difficult to know which suffix to use. Usually, words ending in *se* drop the *e* and use the suffix *-ible*. Words ending in *ge* or *ce* keep the silent *e* and add *-able*. The suffixes *-ary* and *-ery* are often confused, too.

Listed below are pairs of words. Circle the correctly spelled word from each pair. Use your dictionary, if necessary.

1. agreeible   agreeable
2. budgetery   budgetary
3. changeable   changable
4. military   militery
5. monastary   monastery
6. acceptible   acceptable

126

After choosing the correct spelling, use each word in a sentence in the space below.

Choosing the Correct Suffix II

The suffixes *-able* and *-ible* change other parts of speech into adjectives and add the meaning *capable of* or *worthy of*, as in *breakable* (capable of breaking) and *lovable* (worthy of love). It can be difficult to know which suffix to use. Usually, words ending in *se* drop the *e* and use the suffix *-ible*. Words ending in *ge* or *ce* keep the silent *e* and add *-able*. The suffixes *-ary* and *-ery* are often confused, too.

Listed below are pairs of words. Circle the correctly spelled word from each pair. Use your dictionary, if necessary.

1. knowledgeable   knowledgable
2. cemetery   cemetary
3. sensable   sensible
4. trickery   trickary
5. perishable   perishible
6. defensable   defensible

127

The word *station* can use both the suffix *-ery* and the suffix *-ary*, but the two words that result have completely different meanings. In the space below, write the definitions of these two words: *stationery* and *stationary*.

Choosing the Correct Suffix III

The suffixes *-ance* and *-ence* change other parts of speech into nouns and add the meaning *act of* or *quality of*, as in *conveyance* (the act of transporting) and *convenience* (the quality of being suitable or favorable). The suffixes *-ant* and *-ent* can change words into nouns (*attendant*) or adjectives (*hesitant*).

From the pronunciation alone, it can be difficult to determine the spelling of these four suffixes. Occasionally, words end in *-ense*, which has the same pronunciation as *-ance* and *-ence*.

Add a suffix to each word in the list. To be sure of the spelling, use a dictionary.

1. magnific__ __ __

2. off__ __ __ __

3. allow__ __ __ __

4. account__ __ __

5. differ__ __ __ __

6. perman__ __ __

128

Choosing the Correct Suffix IV

The suffixes -ance and -ence change other parts of speech into nouns and add the meaning *act of* or *quality of*, as in *conveyance* (the act of transporting) and *convenience* (the quality of being suitable or favorable). The suffixes -ant and -ent can change words into nouns (*attendant*) or adjectives (*hesitant*).

From the pronunciation alone, it can be difficult to determine the spelling of these four suffixes. Occasionally, words end in -ense, which has the same pronunciation as -ance and -ence.

Add a suffix to each word in the list. To be sure of the spelling, use a dictionary.

1. import__ __ __

2. def__ __ __ __

3. independ__ __ __ __

4. assist__ __ __ __

5. resid__ __ __

The second word above has a different spelling in the United Kingdom and Canada than it does in the United States. Check a dictionary to find how it is spelled in those countries, and write that spelling in the space below.

129

Studying Suffixes 1

The combining forms *-ology* and *-logy* come from the Greek *logos*, meaning *word*. Words ending with these letters usually refer to a science or an area of study. Take the root *graph* (meaning *to write*) and add *-ology*. You have *graphology*, the study of handwriting.

Look up the words below and match each one with its definition. Write the letter of the word on the line to the left of its definition.

a. ornithology   c. numerology   e. oncology

b. pathology   d. theology   f. geology

130

_____ 1. the study of religion and religious beliefs

_____ 2. the study of the causes of illness and disease

_____ 3. the study of numbers and their mystical effect on our lives

_____ 4. the study of birds

_____ 5. the study of tumors (cancer)

Define the word not used in the exercise above.

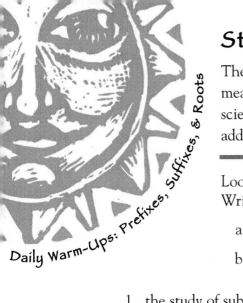

Studying Suffixes II

The combining forms *-ology* and *-logy* come from the Greek *logos*, meaning *word*. Words ending with these letters usually refer to a science or an area of study. Take the root *graph* (meaning *to write*) and add *-ology*. You have *graphology*, the study of handwriting.

Look up the words below and match each one with its definition. Write the letter of the word on the line to the left of its definition.

a. psychology   c. mineralogy

b. genealogy   d. phrenology

_____ 1. the study of substances obtained from the ground

_____ 2. the study of the skull to determine mental ability and character

_____ 3. the study of the human mind and human behavior

_____ 4. the study of the descent of a family or group

The following words have the suffixes *-ology* and *-logy*, but neither refers to an area of study. Look up the definitions of these words: *analogy* and *anthology*.

131

Diagnosing Suffixes 1

Whenever you see the ending *-ectomy* on a word, you can be sure it refers to cutting out or removing something, such as an organ of the body. The suffix *-itis* refers to inflammation or soreness, and *-osis* refers to a diseased condition. Combined with various roots, these suffixes form many medical terms.

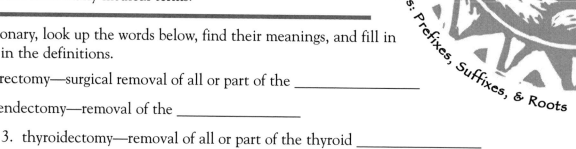

In a dictionary, look up the words below, find their meanings, and fill in the lines in the definitions.

1. gastrectomy—surgical removal of all or part of the _____

2. appendectomy—removal of the _____

3. thyroidectomy—removal of all or part of the thyroid _____

4. leucosis—a diseased condition of the _____

5. halitosis—bad _____ resulting from unhealthy condition of the mouth

6. diverticulosis—a disease of the _____ that results in small pockets being formed along the lining

132

© 2004 Walch Publishing

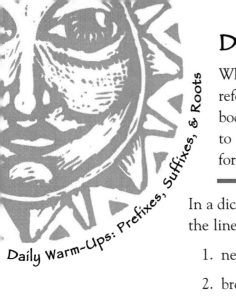

Diagnosing Suffixes II

Whenever you see the ending *-ectomy* on a word, you can be sure it refers to cutting out or removing something, such as an organ of the body. The suffix *-itis* refers to inflammation or soreness, and *-osis* refers to a diseased condition. Combined with various roots, these suffixes form many medical terms.

In a dictionary, look up the words below, find their meanings, and fill in the lines in the definitions.

1. neuritis—inflammation of the _____

2. bronchitis—inflammation of the bronchial _____ in the chest.

3. dermatitis—inflammation of the _____

4. hepatitis—inflammation of the _____

Daily Warm-Ups: Prefixes, Suffixes, & Roots

133

Special Suffixes 1

Sometimes we add suffixes to masculine words to make them feminine, although many people think that this way of altering words is outdated. You may come across these words, though, so you should know what the suffixes mean. Often it is necessary to change the spelling somewhat in the original word.

Write the feminine version of each item below. Use a dictionary, if necessary.

1. waiter   wait_____

2. hero   hero_____

3. aviator   aviat_____

Think about these examples and write at least five other words that change masculine words into feminine ones.

134

Special Suffixes II

Sometimes the suffixes *-ette*, *-et*, *-let*, or *-ling* are added to words to give the meaning *small* to the original work.

Write the small version of each item below.

1. cigar   cigar_____
2. ring   ring_____
3. kitchen   kitchen_____
4. duck   duck_____
5. goose   gos_____

Think about these examples. In the space below, write at least five more words that contain these suffixes. What other meanings do *-ette* and *-ling* have besides *small*? Explain.

135

Special Suffixes III

The suffix *-cide* or *-icide* is added to nouns to refer to the killing of, as in *suicide* (the killing of oneself).

Write a definition for each of the following words.

1. patricide: _____

2. matricide: _____

3. fratricide: _____

4. regicide: _____

    5. infanticide: _____

      6. insecticide: _____

    7. homicide: _____

136

Suffixes Denoting People 1

When you refer to a person from Japan as a Japanese, you are using the suffix *-ese* to mean *one from*. A number of other suffixes are used in the same way.

Write the suffixes in the items below.

1. A person from Israel is an Israel_____.

2. A person from Lebanon is a Leban_____.

3. A person from New York is a New York_____.

4. A person from Texas is a Tex_____.

5. A person from Asia is a Asia_____.

Can you think of other examples of suffixes that denote people? Write at least three sentences in the same format as in the examples above using different suffixes from those already used.

137

Suffixes Denoting People II

When you refer to a person from Japan as a Japanese, you are using the suffix *-ese* to mean *one from*. A number of other suffixes are used in the same way. For some parts of the world, the spelling changes completely.

Can you identify the words to represent persons from the following places?

1. Denmark:

2. Flanders:

3. Afghanistan:

4. Wales:

138

Using Two Suffixes I

Add two or more suffixes to each of the words below. For example, you can take the word *sterile*, add the suffixes *-ize* and *-tion*, and end up with the word *sterilization*.

1. sense

2. joy

3. pure

4. equal

5. book

Write a sentence that includes two or more of the words from the list of words above. Remember to add appropriate suffixes to the endings of the words included.

139

Using Two Suffixes II

Add two or more suffixes to each of the words below. For example, you can take the word *sterile*, add the suffixes *-ize* and *-tion*, and end up with the word *sterilization*.

1. hope

2. class

3. back

4. suit

5. force

Write a sentence that includes two or more of the words from the list of words above. Remember to add appropriate suffixes to the endings of the words included.

Using Two Suffixes III

Add two or more suffixes to each of the words below. For example, you can take the word *sterile*, add the suffixes *-ize* and *-tion*, and end up with the word *sterilization*.

1. help

2. edit

3. drama

4. use

5. part

Write a sentence that includes two or more of the words from the list of words above. Remember to add appropriate suffixes to the endings of the words included.

141

Using Two Suffixes IV

Add two or more suffixes to each of the words below. For example, you can take the word *sterile*, add the suffixes *-ize* and *-tion*, and end up with the word *sterilization*.

1. act

2. friend

3. rely

4. rest

5. create

142

One of the longest words in the English language is antidisestablishmentarianism. List below all the prefixes and suffixes in this word. What is the root?

Prefixes   **Suffixes**

Dropping Suffixes 1

By adding suffixes, we change words to other parts of speech.
Dropping suffixes can do the same.

The list below contains words with suffixes. The suffix in each word is
underlined, and the part of speech follows it. Decide which part of
speech the word will become if you drop the suffix. Then write that
part of speech on the line to the left of the word.

_____ 1. govern<u>ment</u> (noun)

_____ 2. congregation<u>al</u> (adjective)

_____ 3. loose<u>ly</u> (adverb)

_____ 4. weight<u>less</u> (adjective)

_____ 5. persist<u>ence</u> (noun)

Now use three of the suffixed words in sentences of your own.

143

©2004 Walch Publishing

Dropping Suffixes II

By adding suffixes, we change words to other parts of speech. Dropping suffixes can do the same.

The list below contains words with suffixes. The suffix in each word is underlined, and the part of speech follows it. Decide which part of speech the word will become if you drop the suffix. Then write that part of speech on the line to the left of the word.

_____ 1. withdraw<u>al</u> (noun)

_____ 2. help<u>er</u> (noun)

_____ 3. attend<u>ant</u> (noun)

_____ 4. solid<u>ify</u> (verb)

_____ 5. angel<u>ic</u> (adjective)

Now use three of the suffixed words in sentences of your own.

© 2004 Walch Publishing

Dropping Suffixes III

By adding suffixes, we change words to other parts of speech.
Dropping suffixes can do the same.

The list below contains words with suffixes. The suffix in each word is
underlined, and the part of speech follows it. Decide which part of
speech the word will become if you drop the suffix. Then write that
part of speech on the line to the left of the word.

_____ 1. man<u>ly</u> (adjective)

_____ 2. sad<u>ness</u> (noun)

_____ 3. fluf<u>fy</u> (adjective)

_____ 4. refe<u>rence</u> (noun)

_____ 5. nice<u>ty</u> (noun)

Now use three of the suffixed words in sentences
of your own.

145

Inflectional Endings 1

Some letters and groups of letters that we add to the ends of words do not change their parts of speech but perform other functions. These endings are not true suffixes and are usually referred to as *inflectional endings*.

In the following paragraphs, add the proper inflectional endings to the words.

Eddie, suffer_____(1) terribly from the fact that he was short_____(2) than all the other boys in his class, ate spinach, took vitamin_____(3), and drank milk, but it did no good. Even his sister, who was the young_____(4) in the family, was tall_____(5)!

Eddie tri_____(1) to make up for his height in other ways. He studi_____(2) hard, got very good grade_____(3), and join_____(4) the swim team. Soon he was able to swim fast_____(5) than all the team member_____(6).

One day, when Eddie saw a little girl drown_____(1), he jump_____(2) into the water and save_____(3) her life. For this, he was award_____(4) a medal. As he stood on the stage, Eddie felt tall_____(5) than he had ever felt. He had learn_____(6) that there are many way_____(7) to be tall.

Walch Publishing

Daily Warm-Ups: Prefixes, Suffixes, & Roots

Inflectional Endings II

Some letters and groups of letters that we add to the ends of words do not change their parts of speech but perform other functions. For example, when we add *-es* or *-s* to nouns, we form their plurals. By adding *-ing* to verbs (and using auxiliary verbs), we form more tenses. And by adding *-er* or *-est* to adjectives, we form their comparative and superlative forms. These endings are not true suffixes and are usually referred to as *inflectional endings*.

In your own words, write a brief statement explaining how inflectional endings differ from true suffixes. Provide at least ten words with examples of inflectional endings.

147

© 2004 Walch Publishing

Word Elements with Similar Meanings 1

Since our prefixes, roots, and suffixes come from more than one language (primarily Latin and Greek), we have a number of word elements with the same or similar meanings. For example, the prefixes *mono-* and *uni-* refer to *one* (as in *monorail* or *unicycle*).

Below are two lists of prefixes. Draw a line from the words on the left to the words on the right that have similar meanings.

astro	tempo
graph	viv
bio	scrip
chron	stella
photo	lux, luc
anthro	homo

148

Think of words with these prefixes. List at least one word per prefix in the space below.

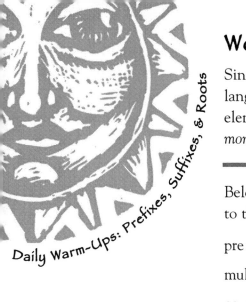

Word Elements with Similar Meanings II

Since our prefixes, roots, and suffixes come from more than one language (primarily Latin and Greek), we have a number of word elements with the same or similar meanings. For example, the prefixes *mono-* and *uni-* refer to *one* (as in *monorail* or *unicycle*).

Below are two lists of prefixes. Draw a line from the words on the left to the words on the right that have similar meanings.

pre	hemi
multi	ante
counter	eu
semi	anti
bene	macro
magni	poly

Think of words with these prefixes. List at least one word per prefix in the space below.

149

Word Elements with Similar Meanings III

Since our prefixes, roots, and suffixes come from more than one language (primarily Latin and Greek), we have a number of word elements with the same or similar meanings. For example, the prefixes *mono-* and *uni-* refer to *one* (as in *monorail* or *unicycle*).

Define each prefix listed below.

1. stella: _____

2. graph: _____

3. viv: _____

4. tempo: _____

5. lux, luc: _____

6. anthro: _____

7. ante: _____

8. poly: _____

9. counter: _____

10. hemi: _____

11. eu: _____

12. macro: _____

13. dis: _____

14. un: _____

150

Word Parts with Opposite Meanings 1

Below are two lists of roots and prefixes. Draw a line from the words on the left to the words on the right that have the opposite meanings.

mono	magni
bene	fin
pre	mal
ex	post
sub	multi
mort	viv
micro	super
ad	de
gen	in

Think of words that include these roots and prefixes. List at least one word per root or prefix in the space below.

151

Word Parts with Opposite Meanings II

Below is a list of roots and prefixes. Define each root or prefix in the space provided.

1. mono: _____

2. ex: _____

3. sub: _____

4. mort: _____

5. ad: _____

6. gen: _____

7. super: _____

8. neo: _____

9. de: _____

10. re: _____

Think about words that contain these roots and prefixes. In the space below, write three sentences with at least one word in each sentence containing a root or prefix from the list above.

152

Word Parts with Two Meanings I

Some prefixes and roots have more than one meaning. For example:

ex-	a. *out*, as in *extract*	b. *former*, as in *ex-teacher*	
homo-	c. *same*, as in *homonym*	d. *human*, as in *homicide*	
dis-	e. *not*, as in *displeased*	f. *apart* or *away*, as in *dismiss*	
in-	g. *not*, as in *inaccurate*	h. *in* or *within*, as in *include*	

Think about the two different meanings for each root or prefix listed above. Then write one sentence for each meaning of each root or prefix in the space below.

153

© 2004 Walch Publishing

Word Elements with Two Meanings II

Some prefixes and roots have more than one meaning. For example:

ex-	a. *out*, as in *extract*	b. *former*, as in *ex-teacher*
homo-	c. *same*, as in *homonym*	d. *human*, as in *homicide*
dis-	e. *not*, as in *displeased*	f. *apart* or *away*, as in *dismiss*
in-	g. *not*, as in *inaccurate*	h. *in* or *within*, as in *include*

In each sentence below, determine the meaning of the underlined prefix or root. Write the letter of the correct meaning on the line at the left.

_____ 1. I will <u>dis</u>pose of this as soon as possible.

_____ 2. How can we <u>ex</u>tricate ourselves from this mess?

_____ 3. The <u>ex</u>-president praised her successor.

_____ 4. I am <u>dis</u>satisfied with that decision.

_____ 5. This method has proved <u>in</u>effective.

_____ 6. Honesty is <u>in</u>grained in his character.

_____ 7. In biology class, we used <u>hom</u>unculus to study the theory of preformation.

_____ 8. Most milk is now <u>homo</u>genized, so the cream doesn't settle on top.

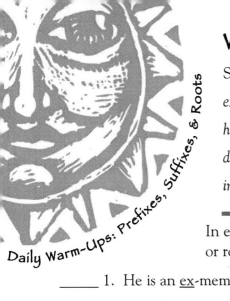

Word Elements with Two Meanings III

Some prefixes and roots have more than one meaning. For example:

ex-	a. *out*, as in *extract*	b. *former*, as in *ex-teacher*
homo-	c. *same*, as in *homonym*	d. *human*, as in *homicide*
dis-	e. *not*, as in *displeased*	f. *apart* or *away*, as in *dismiss*
in-	g. *not*, as in *inaccurate*	h. *in* or *within*, as in *include*

In each sentence below, determine the meaning of the underlined prefix or root. Write the letter of the correct meaning on the line at the left.

_____ 1. He is an <u>ex</u>-member of this society.

_____ 2. I was <u>dis</u>couraged by the low voter turnout.

_____ 3. She was <u>dis</u>charged for chronic tardiness.

_____ 4. Butter is a basic <u>in</u>gredient of puff pastry.

_____ 5. They are such good friends that they are almost <u>in</u>separable.

_____ 6. We <u>ex</u>pel carbon dioxide when we breathe.

_____ 7. The students were grouped <u>homo</u>geneously according to their interests.

_____ 8. The researchers found the bones of an early <u>hom</u>inid at the site.

155

Word Analysis 1

When you come across a word you don't know, recognizing a prefix, suffix, or root in the word can help you figure out the word's meaning.

In the sentences below, look for elements of the underlined words that you recognize, and try to figure out the words' meanings. Check them in a dictionary. Write their definitions under each sentence.

Write if each sentence is true (**T**) or false (**F**) on the line provided.

_____ 1. The United States is a <u>polyglot</u> nation.
polyglot:

_____ 2. The wheel is an <u>innovation</u> of the twentieth century.
innovation:

_____ 3. Andrew Carnegie, who donated millions of dollars to the establishment of libraries, was a real <u>philanthropist</u>.
philanthropist:

_____ 4. When you use <u>malapropisms</u>, people will consider you intelligent.
malapropisms:

156

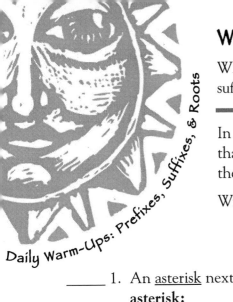

Word Analysis II

When you come across a word you don't know, recognizing a prefix, suffix, or root in the word can help you figure out the word's meaning.

In the sentences below, look for elements of the underlined words that you recognize, and try to figure out the words' meanings. Check them in a dictionary. Write their definitions under each sentence.

Write if each sentence is true (**T**) or false (**F**) on the line provided.

_____ 1. An <u>asterisk</u> next to a word may indicate a footnote on the page.
asterisk:

_____ 2. Short words such as *an* and *the* are called <u>sesquipedalians</u>.
sesquipedalians:

_____ 3. A person who is <u>gregarious</u> could be described as a loner.
gregarious:

_____ 4. Most countries are ruled by a single leader rather than by a <u>triumvirate</u>.
triumvirate:

157

Word Analysis III

When you come across a word you don't know, recognizing a prefix, suffix, or root in the word can help you figure out the word's meaning.

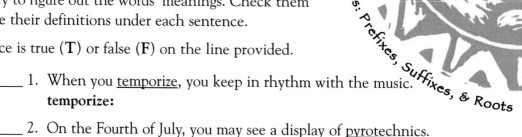

In the sentences below, look for elements of the underlined words that you recognize, and try to figure out the words' meanings. Check them in a dictionary. Write their definitions under each sentence.

Write if each sentence is true (**T**) or false (**F**) on the line provided.

_____ 1. When you <u>temporize</u>, you keep in rhythm with the music.
   temporize:

_____ 2. On the Fourth of July, you may see a display of <u>pyrotechnics</u>.
   pyrotechnics:

_____ 3. A <u>bibliophile</u> spends leisure time looking over rare stamps.
   bibliophile:

_____ 4. An <u>expatriate</u> is a person who has left his or her homeland.
   expatriate:

158

Word Analysis IV

When you come across a word you don't know, you can often figure out its meaning from recognizable elements and the context of the word.

The underlined words below contain elements you have studied. Try to guess the meaning of each word. Write your ideas in the space provided under each sentence.

1. Fireflies are unusual because they produce <u>bioluminescence</u>.

2. Some people believed that everything on the earth originated from four elements—fire, air, earth, and water. The fifth element, <u>quintessence</u>, was the matter of heavenly bodies.

3. Around the sun and other stars, there is a <u>chromosphere</u> consisting chiefly of hydrogen gas.

4. The alchemists of the Middle Ages believed in the <u>transmutation</u> of base metals into gold and silver.

Word Analysis V

When you come across a word you don't know, you can often figure out its meaning from recognizable elements and the context of the word.

The underlined words below contain elements you have studied. Try to guess the meaning of each word. Write your ideas in the space provided under each sentence.

1. The evidence in this case is <u>incontrovertible</u>.

2. As long as you have your passport, no further <u>verification</u> is necessary.

3. The <u>convocation</u> of graduating seniors will be held on May 10.

4. For the patient with high blood pressure, the doctor prescribed an <u>antihypertensive</u>.

160

Word Analysis VI

When you come across a word you don't know, you can often figure out its meaning from recognizable elements and the context of the word.

The underlined words below contain elements you have studied. Try to guess the meaning of each word. Write your ideas in the space provided under each sentence.

1. The archeologists discovered the skeleton of a <u>hominid</u>.

2. He has a natural <u>proclivity</u> for music.

3. The laws of physics are <u>immutable</u>.

4. The <u>secessionists</u> urged the South to break away from the Union and form a confederacy.

161

Mathematical Terms 1

Each of the words in the sentences below is missing a prefix, a root, or a suffix. The meaning of the missing element is underlined in the sentence. Fill in the missing elements on the line provided.

1. If you <u>measure</u> the distance through a circle from side to side, you find its dia_____.

2. The distance <u>around</u> the outside of a circle is its _____ference.

3. _____metry is the study of the properties of, measurement of, and relationships between objects on the <u>earth</u> and in space.

4. <u>Half</u> of a sphere is a _____sphere.

5. When you make a mathematical statement and then test it to show that it has the <u>quality of</u> truth, you are testing its valid_____.

6. Lines that come <u>together</u> at a single point are said to _____verge.

162

Mathematical Terms II

Each of the words in the sentences below is missing a prefix, a root, or a suffix. The meaning of the missing element is underlined in the sentence. Fill in the missing elements on the line provided.

1. <u>That</u> <u>which</u> is divided into the dividend in a division problem is the divis_____.

2. When you cut an angle in <u>two</u>, you _____sect it.

3. When we say that five per_____ of a certain number is twenty, we mean that twenty represents five parts out of the whole of one <u>hundred</u> parts.

4. A mathematical statement that shows the <u>condition of</u> two sets of figures being equal (and having an equal sign between them) is an equa_____.

5. In the math problem 32×12, you are increasing the original amount (32) <u>many</u> times, or _____plying it.

163

Mathematical Terms III

An example of a mathematical word with a suffix is *fraction*.

In the space below, list other mathematical terms that contain word parts you have studied. Think about the definition of each term. How does the prefix, suffix, or root contribute to the meaning? Using the list you have created, write three sentences below.

164

Word Elements in Names 1

Some dictionaries contain lists of boys' and girls' names and their meanings. Glance through one of these books, and find examples of names that contain the roots, prefixes, and suffixes you have been studying, as well as other prefixes and suffixes. Here is an example to get you started.

Names with Greek or Latin Roots:

Bene<u>dict</u> (It also has a prefix— -bene.)

165

Word Elements in Names II

Some dictionaries contain lists of boys' and girls' names and their meanings. Glance through one of these books, and find examples of names that contain the roots, prefixes, and suffixes you have been studying, as well as other prefixes and suffixes. Here is an example to get you started.

Names with Greek or Latin Prefixes:

<u>Oct</u>avius

166

Word Elements in Names III

Some dictionaries contain lists of boys' and girls' names and their meanings. Glance through one of these books, and find examples of names that contain the roots, prefixes, and suffixes you have been studying, as well as other prefixes and suffixes. Here is an example to get you started.

Names with Greek or Latin Suffixes:

Clar<u>ence</u> (It also has a root—clar.)

167

New Expressions 1

Some of our recently developed expressions use the prefixes and suffixes you have studied (*teleconference*, to *Americanize*, and so forth). Others use suffix-like endings that are not true suffixes (such as *Koreagate*).

Select word parts from the list that fit into the words below. In the space at the left, write the letter of the item you have selected for each pair of words.

a. -athon   d. petro-

b. mini-   e. -off

c. micro-   f. -aholic

_____ 1. a lengthy event, usually for raising funds for some charity— bike_____, walk_____

_____ 2. a small nuclear weapon— _____nuke

a short set of dramatizations— _____series

_____ 3. wealth derived from oil— _____dollars

power held by the oil-producing countries— _____power

168

New Expressions II

Some of our recently developed expressions use the prefixes and suffixes you have studied (*teleconference*, to *Americanize*, and so forth). Others use suffix-like endings that are not true suffixes (such as *Koreagate*).

Select word parts from the list that fit into the words below. In the space at the left, write the letter of the item you have selected for each pair of words.

a. -athon   d. -off

b. petro-   e. eco-

c. non-   f. -aholic

_____ 1. one addicted to the game of golf—golf_____

one addicted to chocolate—choc_____.

_____ 2. a contest—cook_____, bake_____

_____ 3. one overly concerned about ecology— _____freak.

prediction of disaster if ecology is ignored— _____doom.

169

New Expressions III

Some of our recently developed expressions use the prefixes and suffixes you have studied (*teleconference*, to *Americanize*, and so forth.). Others use suffix-like endings that are not true suffixes (such as *Koreagate*).

Select word parts from the list that fit into the words below. On the line at the left, write the letter of the item you have selected for each pair of words.

a. mega- d. petro-

b. mini- e. non-

c. micro- f. de-

170

_____ 1. the selling off of items in a collection— _____accession

the release of a person from an institution— _____institutionalization

_____ 2. a piece of silicon used as a processing unit in a computer— _____chip

to publish something on microfilm— _____publish

_____ 3. a very large dose (of vitamins, drugs, and so forth)— _____dose

a very large oil tanker— _____tanker

Test: Roots 1

On the line at the left, write the letter of the root that refers to each of the following:

_____ 1. sight   a. aud   b. vid   c. gen

_____ 2. time   a. thermo   b. tempo   c. tract

_____ 3. speech   a. dic   b. dec   c. derm

_____ 4. trust   a. fin   b. fid   c. flu

_____ 5. stars   a. avi   b. agri   c. astro

In the space below, write some examples of the correct roots used in the above exercise.

171

Test: Roots II

On the line at the left, write the letter of the root that refers to each of the following:

_____ 1. feet   a. port   b. ped   c. pyr

_____ 2. life   a. viv   b. voc   c. ven

_____ 3. stone   a. log   b. laud   c. lith

_____ 4. blood   a. homo   b. hemo   c. hydr

_____ 5. color   a. chrom   b. cor   c. cred

In the space below, write some examples of the correct roots used in the above exercise.

172

Test: Prefixes 1

On the line at the left, write the letter of the prefix that refers to each of the following:

_____ 1. opposite of pre-   a. post-   b. sub-   c. pro-

_____ 2. opposite of bene-   a. mis-   b. mal-   c. mid-

_____ 3. opposite of micro-   a. mono-   b. mille-   c. magni-

_____ 4. same as dis-   a. anti-   b. in-   c. neo-

_____ 5. same as poly-   a. tri-   b. multi-   c. bi-

In the space below, write some examples of words that use the prefixes shown in the above exercise.

173

Test: Prefixes II

On the line at the left, write the letter of the prefix that refers to each of the following:

_____ 1. same as mono-   a. uni-   b. di-   c. quad-

_____ 2. the largest   a. dec-   b. cent-   c. kilo-

_____ 3. the longest time   a. semi-annual   b. biennial   c. annual
      period

_____ 4. the most sides   a. octagon   b. pentagon   c. hexagon

_____ 5. suggests cooperation a. contr-   b. con-, com- c. anti-

In the space below, write some examples of words that use the prefixes shown in the exercise above.

174

Test: Suffixes 1

On the line at the left, write the correct answer.

_____ 1. suffix added to *human*   a. -ish   b. -kind   c. -ly
     to produce a noun

_____ 2. suffix added to *secure*   a. -ly   b. -ity   c. -ing
     to produce an adverb

_____ 3. added to *drama*   a. -tist   b. -ic   c. -ize
     to produce a verb

_____ 4. added to *office*   a. -ial   b. -er   c. -iate
     to produce an adjective

_____ 5. added to *kind*   a. -er   b. -ly   c. -ness
     to produce a noun

In the space below, write some examples of words that use the suffixes shown in the exercise above.

175

Test Suffixes II

On the line at the left, write the correct answer.

_____ 1. suffix referring   a. -itis   b. -ology   c. -ectomy
       to surgery

_____ 2. suffix referring   a. -ess   b. -ette   c. -ate
       to something small

_____ 3. suffix likely to refer   a. -ism   b. -dom   c. -or
       to a person

_____ 4. suffix used most often   a. -ic   b. -ly   c. -ity
       in forming adverbs

In the space below, write some examples of words that use the suffixes shown in the exercise above.

176

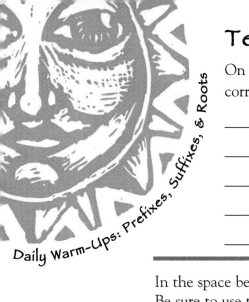

Test: Spelling 1

On the line at the left, write the letter of the word that is spelled correctly.

_____ 1.   a. sensable   b. sensible

_____ 2.   a. artisticly   b. artistically

_____ 3.   a. dissatisfied   b. disatisfied

_____ 4.   a. non-British   b. nonbritish

_____ 5.   a. proceed   b. procede

In the space below, write a sentence for each word used in the exercise above. Be sure to use the correct spelling for each word.

177

Test: Spelling II

On the line at the left, write the letter of the word that is spelled correctly.

_____ 1.   a. iluminate   b. illuminate

_____ 2.   a. selfdiscipline   b. self-discipline

_____ 3.   a. perishible   b. perishable

_____ 4.   a. dictionary   b. dictionery

_____ 5.   a. allowance   b. allowence

In the space below, write a sentence for each word used in the above exercise. Be sure to use the correct spelling for each word.

178

Challenge 1

Listed below are some roots and their meanings. Some roots may be new to you.

Root	Meaning
arch	chief, first, rule
belli	war
clam, claim	cry out
endo	within
magn	great
pel	drive, urge
scope	see, watch
vac	empty

In the space below, write examples of words that contain each root. Write as many examples as you can think of.

179

Challenge 11

Here are some prefixes and suffixes that may be new to you. Look at the prefix or suffix and the meaning.

Prefix	Meaning	Suffix	Meaning
audio-	hear	-ile	relating to, suited for, capable of
bio-	life	-nomy	law
epi-	upon, over	-some	like, tending to
vide-, vis-	see	-tude	state of, condition of

180

In the space below, write examples of words that contain each prefix and suffix. Write as many examples as you can think of.

1. 1. d; 2. e; 3. a; 4. f; 5. c
2. 1. d; 2. b; 3. f; 4. a; 5. c
3. 1. e; 2. b; 3. d; 4. a; 5. f
4. 1. b; 2. a; 3. d; 4. c; 5. f
5. 1. verb; 2. noun; 3. adverb; 4. adjective; 5. adjective; 6. adjective
6. 1. verb; 2. noun; 3. adverb or adjective; 4. noun; 5. noun; 6. adjective
7. 1. astro; 2. temp; 3. man; 4. avi; Sentences will vary.
8. 1. biblo; 2. photo; 3. homo; 4. geo; Sentences will vary.
9. 1. scrip; 2. ped; 3. hort; 4. zo; Sentences will vary.
10. Answers will vary.
11. 1. educate; 2. reducing; 3. product; 4. introduce; Sentences will vary.
12. 1. conductor; 2. deduction; 3. inducement; 4. ductless; Words will vary.
13. Words and paragraphs will vary.
14. Words will vary.
15. 1. b; 2. d; 3. c; 4. a; Sentences will vary.
16. 1. b; 2. a; 3. c; 4. d; Sentences will vary.

17. Prefixes *male-* (*bad*) and *bene-* (*good*) added to the root *dic* create words of opposite meaning. *Malediction* refers to a curse, while *benediction* refers to a blessing. Additional words will vary.
18. 1. conspicuous; 2. circumspect; 3. periscope; 4. videotape; 5. kaleidoscope
19. 1. perspective; 2. radarscope; 3. vista; 4. horoscope; 5. spectrum
20. 1. gastroscope; 2. visionary; 3. specter; 4. evidence; 5. visor
21. adventure, venture, convinced, videotape, visualize, invincible, victory, vocal
22. vocation, vitality, vitamin, survive, revive, avocation, envision, visible, veritable, verify
23. con<u>tract</u>, de<u>tract</u>, ex<u>tract</u>, re<u>tract</u>, <u>tract</u>or, con<u>tract</u>or, dis<u>tract</u>ed, pro<u>tract</u>ed, <u>tract</u>ion
24. tractor, traction, distracted, contractor
25. com<u>mit</u>ted, <u>miss</u>ile, o<u>mit</u>ted, re<u>miss</u>ion, trans<u>miss</u>ion, dis<u>miss</u>ed, <u>miss</u>ive, per<u>mit</u>, re<u>mit</u>
26. permit, transmission, dismissed, committed
27. adj<u>ect</u>ive, de<u>ject</u>ed, in<u>ject</u>ed, pro<u>ject</u>, re<u>ject</u>, con<u>ject</u>ure, e<u>ject</u>, inter<u>ject</u>ion, pro<u>ject</u>ile

Daily Warm-Ups: Prefixes, Suffixes, & Roots

28. adjective, dejected, project, reject
29. Definitions will vary.
30. fluctuate, affluent, influx, fluent
31. de<u>flect</u>, <u>flex</u>ible, <u>flex</u>uous, genu<u>flect</u>, re<u>flex</u>, <u>flex</u>ed, <u>flex</u>or, in<u>flec</u>tion, re<u>flec</u>tion; Definitions will vary.
32. reflection, flexed, inflection, deflect; Sentences will vary.
33. 1. convention; 2. chromatics; 3. interjection; 4. pacifier; 5. synchronize; 6. vocation; Sentences will vary.
34. 1. remittance; 2. sophistry; 3. epidermis; 4. scribble; 5. renovate; 6. mortification; 7. confidant(e); Sentences will vary.
35. 1. manuscript; 2. sphygmomanometer; 3. mortician; 4. aviary; Roots and words will vary.
36. 1. astronomical; 2. agronomist; 3. phototropism; 4. phonetics; Roots and words will vary.
37. 1. pedestal; 2. transcript; 3. sophisticated; 4. spectator; Roots and words will vary.
38. 1. bibliography, biblical; 2. incorporate, corpse; Words, definitions, and sentences will vary.
39. 1. finale, finalize; 2. dehydrated, hydroelectric; Words, definitions, and sentences will vary.
40. 1. lucid, Lucite; 2. transmutation, immutable; Words, definitions, and sentences will vary.
41. 1. genes, regenerated; 2. tortuous, contortionist; Words, definitions, and sentences will vary.
42. 1. prove that it is <u>true</u>; 2. full of <u>life</u>; 3. <u>endless</u>; Words, definitions, and sentences will vary.
43. 1. the <u>same</u> in sound; 2. plants that live in <u>water</u>; 3. that the <u>earth</u> was the center of the universe; Words, definitions, and sentences will vary.
44. 1. <u>sounds</u> of the letters; 2. one skilled with <u>plants</u>; 3. an instrument for measuring the altitude of the sun and <u>stars</u>; Words, definitions, and sentences will vary.
45. 1. one who <u>looks</u> within himself or herself; 2. the formal statement (what the council <u>said</u>); Words will vary.
46. 1. the age when dinosaurs and other reptiles were the supreme <u>animals</u>; 2. turning to the <u>light</u>; Words will vary.
47. 1. One who tries to attract <u>people</u> to gain power; 2. difficult, with many <u>twists</u> and turns; Words will vary.
48. 1. b; 2. d; 3. a; 4. c; Definitions will vary.

Daily Warm-Ups: Prefixes, Suffixes, & Roots

49. 1. a; 2. d; 3. b; 4. c; Definitions will vary.
50. 1. a; 2. c; 3. b; 4. d; Definitions will vary.
51. a. 5; b. 2; c. 3; d. 1; e. 4; Sentences will vary.
52. a. 1; b. 4; c. 5; d. 3; e. 2; Sentences will vary.
53. a. 2; b. 3; c. 5; d. 4; e. 1; Sentences will vary.
54. a. 2; b. 1; c. 4; d. 3; e. 5; Sentences will vary.
55. 1. archbishop, auditorium; 2. seniority, recession; 3. constructing, thermopane; 4. legal, clarity; 5. stabilizing, positions
56. 1. tenant, depends; 2. unconscious, dialogue; 3. laudable, granolith; 4. Anthropoid, protect; 5. cardiograph, hemotoma
57. 1. f; 2. h; 3. i; 4. k; 5. a; Words will vary.
58. 1. g; 2. b; 3. c; 4. d; 5. j; 6. e; Sentences will vary.
59. 1. procession; 2. motivate; 3. recede; 4. successor; 5. supersede
60. 1. motive; 2. concede; 3. movement; 4. intercede; 5. movable; 6. commotion
61. 1. pain; 2. death; 3. animals; 4. speaking; panphobia: fear of everything; Definitions and sentences will vary.
62. 1. heights; 2. blood; 3. poison; 4. water; Phobias and definitions will vary.
63. 1. correspond; 2. compromise; 3. conference; 4. contributed; Words will vary.
64. 1. adhere; 2. adapt; 3. admit; Definitions and examples will vary.
65. 1. divert; 2. deported; 3. decayed; 4. dispel; Examples will vary.
66. 1. permission; 2. perfume; 3. reopened; 4. repellant; Examples will vary.
67. 1. monologue; 2. circumambulate; 3. quadruped; 4. subterranean; 5. disharmonious; 6. intra-urban
68. 1. counterespionage; 2. polygon; 3. semicircle; 4. microtome; 5. tricorn; 6. predict; 7. recompense
69. 1. telemetry; 2. international; 3. autobiography; 4. extricate; 5. superior; 6. antebellum; 7. extraterrestrial
70. 1. dishonest; 2. retread; 3. overreacted; 4. forefinger; 5. incorrect; Sentences will vary.
71. 1. midday; 2. postgraduate; 3. predetermined; 4. transatlantic; 5. inconspicuous; Sentences will vary.
72. 1. disobey; 2. postscript; 3. midair; 4. transcontinental; 5. refuel; Sentences will vary.

Daily Warm-Ups: Prefixes, Suffixes, & Roots

73. 1. overslept; 2. predominant; 3. disagree;
    4. foreword; 5. postmortem; Sentences will vary.
74. 1. foreground; 2. midpoint; 3. ineffective;
    4. rediscover; 5. overtime; Sentences will vary.
75. 1. excavate; 2. extrasensory; 3. equilibrium;
    4. telephoto; 5. trans-Siberian; Sentences will vary.
76. 1. trilateral; 2. supersede; 3. subordinate;
    4. semiannual; 5. admonish; Sentences will vary.
77. 1. antiaircraft; 2. autonomous; 3. malaria;
    4. misdemeanor; 5. midrib; Sentences will vary.
78. Illustrations should clearly show each word; Words will vary.
79. Illustrations should clearly show each word; Words will vary.
80. 1. bicep: a muscle having two heads; 2. centavo: 1/100 of a peso (in Mexican money); 3. decathlon: an athletic contest consisting of 10 events; 4. duplex: a two-unit apartment; 5. millipede: a small animal with many legs (supposedly 1,000); Sentences will vary.
81. 1. monochromatic: consisting of one color;

2. octodont: having eight teeth; 3. septennial: lasting seven years or occurring every seven years; 4. sexagenarian: a person over 60 years in age but under 70; 5. trefoil: a plant with three leaves on a stem, such as clover; Sentences will vary.
82. 1. 4; 2. 1; 3. 9; 4. 6; 5. 2; 6. 7; 7. 5; 8. 3; 9. 8
83. 1. decagon: a figure with 10 sides; 2. decalogue: a set of rules with binding authority; 3. decameter: a line of verse with 10 metrical feet; 4. decapod: an animal with 10 legs or arms, such as a squid; Sentences will vary.
84. 1. under; 2. of lower rank; 3. somewhat; 4. under; 5. somewhat; 6. below; 7. near; Sentences will vary.
85. 1. part of; 2. under; 3. part of; 4. of lower rank than; 5. under
86. 1. superpower; 2. hypercritical; 3. extracurricular; 4. hypertension; 5. supernatural; 6. extraordinary; 7. extraterrestrial
87. 1. superfluous; 2. hyperventilation; 3. extrasensory; 4. superstructure; 5. Hyperopia; 6. hyperglycemia; 7. extravagance; 8. superhuman

88. 1. enforce; 2. refill; 3. befriend; Rhymes will vary.
89. 1. declare; 2. withdraw; 3. embark
90. Adverbs and sentences will vary.
91. All of the words are spelled correctly except 6 and 8. Definitions will vary.
92. All of the words are spelled correctly except 5 and 6. Definitions will vary.
93. All of the words are spelled correctly except 1, 3, and 5. Definitions will vary.
94. All of the words are spelled correctly except 1, 3, and 7. Definitions will vary.
95. 1. exposition; 2. ex-soldier; Answers will vary.
96. 1. selfless; 2. self-sufficient; Answers will vary.
97. 1. panchromatic; 2. Pan-Islamic; Answers will vary.
98. 1. non-Roman; 2. nonaddictive; Answers will vary.
99. 1. coagulate; 2. co-agents; Answer: to prevent mispronunciation when you first glance at the word
100. 1. re-form; 2. reform; Answers will vary.
101. 1. festive; 2 repulsive; 3. apprehensive; 4. courageous; 5. boisterous; 6. ridiculous;

Sentences will vary.
102. 1. reliable; 2. charitable; 3. amiable; 4 fearless; 5. ruthless; 6. spineless; Sentences will vary.
103. 1. graceful; 2. spiteful; 3. helpful; 4. obstinate; 5. compassionate; 6. fortunate; Sentences will vary.
104. 1. exotic; 2. sympathetic; 3. antagonistic; 4. fragrant; 5. tolerant; 6. exuberant; Sentences will vary.
105. 1. foolish; 2. purplish; 3. Turkish; 4. traditional; 5. topical; 6. fictional; Sentences will vary.
106. 1. frighten; 2. familiarize; 3. beautify; 4. twinkle; 5. generalize; Words will vary.
107. 1. fabricate; 2. buckle; 3. lessen; 4. mystify; 5. liberate
108. 1. criticize; 2. justify; 3. formulate; 4. terrorize; 5. magnify; Words will vary.
109. 1. -ty; 2. -ate; 3. -ist; 4. -or; 5. -ship; 6. -hood; 7. -ance
110. 1. -ism; 2. -ness; 3. -ant; 4. -tion; 5. -age; 6. -sion; 7. -ee
111. 1. electrically; 2. formally; 3. nicely; 4. frantically;

5. magically; 6. freely; 7. beautifully; Examples of words will vary.
112. 1. tenderly; 2. energetically; 3. electrically; 4. gradually; 5. confidentially; 6. artistically; 7. publicly
113. 1. novelist, novelty, nouns; 2. helpful, helpless, adjectives; 3. employee, employer, nouns; 4. kindness, noun, kindly, adjective, adverb
114. 1. attention, noun, attentive, adjective; 2. terminate, verb, terminal, noun, adjective; 3. memorize, verb, memory, noun; 4. dependable, adjective, dependent, noun, adjective
115. Some words from the root *dent* include: dental, dentist, denture, dentifrice, dentine, dentistry, and dentition. The word *edentulous* means *toothless*.
116. 1. courageous; 2. skyward; 3. championship; 4. singer; 5. knowingly; 6. motorist; Ask the students this question: Which suffix on the list forms adjectives in some instances, but is usually used to form adverbs? Answer: -ly; Adjective examples: curly, friendly; Adverb examples: slowly,

nicely
117. 1. farmer; 2. homeward; 3. idealist; 4. workmanship; 5. unlikely; 6. clamorous; Words will vary.
118. 1. westward; 2. violinist; 3. dangerous; 4. eventually; 5. teacher; 6. friendship; Words will vary.
119. 1. hardship; 2. seaward; 3. poisonous; 4. immediately; 5. receptionist; 6. designer; Words will vary.
120. 1. noun; 2. verb; 3. adverb; 4. adverb; 5. adjective; 6. adjective; 7. adjective; 8. adjective; from Latin *suffixus*, to fasten underneath
121. 1. noun; 2. verb; 3. verb; 4. noun; 5. adverb; 6. verb; 7. noun; 8. adverb
122. 1. breakage; 2. attendance; 3. freedom; 4. absentee; 5. waiter; 6. statehood; 7. situation; 8. Hinduism; 9. cyclist; 10. solemnity
123. 1. movable; 2. national; 3. skillful; 4. restless; 5. angelic; 6. marvelous; 7. foolish; 8. dominate; 9. Moisten; 10. purify
124. 1. hypnotist; 2. hypnotize; 3. hypnotic;

4. friendship; 5. friendly; 6. friendless; Suffixes will vary.

125. 1. attractive; 2. attraction; 3. lovable; 4. lover; 5. electricity; 6. electrician; Suffixes will vary.

126. 1. agreeable; 2. budgetary; 3. changeable; 4. military; 5. monastery; 6. acceptable; Suffixes will vary.

127. 1. knowledgeable; 2. cemetery; 3. sensible; 4. trickery; 5. perishable; 6. defensible; stationery: materials used for writing; stationary: immobile

128. 1. magnificent; 2. offense; 3. allowance; 4. accountant; 5. different; 6. permanent

129. 1. important; 2. defense; 3. independence; 4. assistant; 5. resident; defence

130. 1. d; 2. b; 3. c; 4. a; 5. e; geology—the study of the earth

131. 1. c; 2. d; 3. a; 4. b; analogy: comparison, similarity; anthology: a collection of poems or other writings by a number of authors

132. 1. stomach; 2. appendix; 3. gland; 4. blood; 5. breath; 6. intestines

133. 1. nerves; 2. tubes; 3. skin; 4. liver

134. 1. waitress; 2. heroine; 3. aviatrix;

135. 1. cigarette; 2. ringlet; 3. kitchenette; 4. duckling; 5. gosling; Ette can mean imitation, as in leatherette, or a group, as in octette and sextet. Ling can mean having the quality of, as in hireling, or in the manner of, as in sideling.

136. 1. murder of one's father; 2. murder of one's mother; 3. murder of one's brother or sister; 4. murder of a king; 5. murder of a baby; 6. killing of insects; 7. murder of a human being

137. 1. Israeli; 2. Lebanese; 3. New Yorker; 4. Texan; 5. Asian; Sentences will vary.

138. 1. Danes; 2. Flemings; 3. Afgans; 4. Welshmen or Welshwomen

139. 1. sensational; 2. joyfully; 3. purification; 4. equalization; 5. bookishness; Sentences will vary.

140. The following are examples of answers that may be given. 1. hopefulness; 2. classification; 3. backwardness; 4. suitability; 5. forcefulness

141. The following are examples of answers that may be given. 1. helplessness; 2. editorial;

Daily Warm-Ups: Prefixes, Suffixes, & Roots

3. dramatically; 4. usefulness; 5. partially; Sentences will vary.

142. The following are examples of answers that may be given. 1. activity; 2. friendliness; 3. reliability; 4. restlessness; 5. creativity; Antidisestablishmentarianism may be considered to have three prefixes and four suffixes, since the root originally was *stabilis*. It may also be consid- ered as having only two prefixes, if one accepts *establish* as the root. Actually, though, the *e* in *establish* was originally a prefix.

143. 1. verb; 2. noun; 3. adjective; 4. noun; 5. verb; Sentences will vary.

144 1. verb; 2. verb or noun; 3. verb; 4. adjective or noun; 5. noun; Sentences will vary.

145. 1. noun or verb; 2. adjective; 3. noun or verb; 4. verb; 5. adjective; Sentences will vary.

146. Paragraph one 1. suffering; 2. shorter; 3. vitamins; 4. youngest; 5. taller; Paragraph two 1. tried; 2. studied; 3. grades; 4. joined; 5. faster; 6. members; Paragraph three 1. drowning;

2. jumped; 3. saved; 4. awarded; 5. taller; 6. learned; 7. ways

147. Inflectional endings do not change the part of speech, but they can change the tense or create comparative and superlative forms. words will vary.

148.
astro–stella	astronomy, stellar
graph–scrip	script, graphic
bio–viv	biology, vivid
chron–tempo	chronology, temporary
photo–lux, luc	photography, luxury or lucid
anthro–homo	homogeneous, anthropology

149.
pre–ante	present, antecedent
multi–poly	multiply, polynomial
counter–anti	antibiotic, counterclockwise
semi–hemi	semiformal, hemisphere
bene–eu	beneficial, euphoria
magni–macro	magnify, macrocosm

Words will vary.

150. 1. stella: star; 2. graph: write; 3. viv: life; 4. tempo: time; 5. lux, luc: light; 6. anthro: man; 7. ante: before; 8. poly: many; 9. counter: against;

Daily Warm-Ups: Prefixes, Suffixes, & Roots

10. hemi: half; 11. eu: good, well; 12. macro: large, great; 13. dis: not; 14. un: not

151.

mono–multi	monotheistic, multidimensional
bene–mal	beneficial, malevolent
pre–post	present, postwar
ex–in	extra, inside
sub–super	subgroup, superhero
mort–viv	mortality, vivacious
micro–magni	microscope, magnitude
ad–de	additive, demolish
gen–fin	generation, final

152. 1. mono: one; 2. ex: out of; 3. sub: under, below; 4. mort: death; 5. ad: to, toward; 6. gen: birth, beginning; 7. super: higher in quantity or quality; 8. neo: new; 9. de: away from, take away; 10. re: again or new; Sentences will vary.

153. Sentences will vary.

154. 1. f; 2. a; 3. b; 4. e; 5. g; 6. h; 7. d; 8. c

155. 1. b; 2. e; 3. f; 4. h; 5. g; 6. a; 7. c; 8. h

156. 1. T; polyglot: consisting of persons who speak many different languages; 2. F; innovation: new device/invention; 3. T; philanthropist: one who promotes human welfare; 4. F; malapropisms: words that are misused in place of similar-sounding terms.

157. 1. T; asterisk: a small star used as a reference mark in printing; 2. F; sesquipedalians: long words (literally means a foot-and-a-half long); 3. F; gregarious: very sociable; 4. T; triumvirate: a group of three

158. 1. F; temporize: delay in order to gain time; to put off until later; 2. T; pyrotechnics: fireworks; 3. F; bibliophile: lover of books; 4. T; expatriate: one who leaves his or her native country for another

159. 1. light from chemicals within their bodies; 2. a fifth essence or basic substance; 3. a ring of bright color; 4. a change from one metal into another

160. 1. unchangeable, undeniable; 2. proof; 3. meeting; 4. a drug that counteracts the effects of high blood pressure

161. 1. manlike creature; 2. inclination, leaning toward; 3. unchangeable; 4. one who advocates a separation

Daily Warm-Ups: Prefixes, Suffixes, & Roots

162. 1. diameter; 2. circumference; 3. Geometry;
      4. hemisphere; 5. validity; 6. converge
163. 1. divisor; 2. bisect; 3. percent; 4. equation;
      5. multiplying
164. Extra terms that might be listed: decimal, triangle,
      numerator, product, intersect, vertical, centimeter,
      polyhedron, hypotenuse, billion
165. Some names with roots: <u>St</u>ella, <u>Av</u>is, <u>Man</u>uel,
      <u>Clar</u>ice, <u>Fid</u>elia, <u>Ver</u>a, <u>Phil</u>ip, <u>Vict</u>or
166. Some names with prefixes: <u>Con</u>stance, <u>Magn</u>us,
      Eugene, <u>Non</u>a
167. Some names with suffixes: Prud<u>ence</u>, Pati<u>ence</u>,
      Nest<u>or</u>, Hect<u>or</u>, Sylvest<u>er</u>, Flori<u>an</u>
168. 1. a; 2. b; 3. d
169. 1. f; 2. d; 3. e
170. 1. f; 2. c; 3. a
171. 1. b; 2. b; 3. a; 4. b; 5. c; Examples will vary.
172. 1. b; 2. a; 3. c; 4. b; 5. a; Examples will vary.
173. 1. a; 2. b; 3. c; 4. b; 5. b; Examples will vary.
174. 1. a; 2. c; 3. b; 4. a; 5. b; Examples will vary.

175. 1. b; 2. a; 3. c; 4. a; 5. c; Examples will vary.
176. 1. c; 2. b; 3. c; 4. b; Examples will vary.
177. 1. b; 2. b; 3. a; 4. a; 5. a; Sentences will vary.
178. 1. a; 2. b; 3. b; 4. a; 5. a; Sentences will vary.
179. Examples: arch: architect, archaic, monarchy,
      archangel; belli: rebellion, belligerent, bellicose;
      clam, claim: exclamation, clamor, proclamation,
      acclaim; endo: endorse, endocardial, endoskeleton,
      endosperm; magn: magnify, magnificent,
      magnitude; pel: compel, dispel, repel, impulse;
      scope: telescope, microscope, periscope; vac:
      vacate, vacuum, evacuate, vacant
180. Prefix examples: audio: audiometer, auditory,
      audiophile; bio: biology, biography, biosphere; epi:
      epidemic, epidermis, epitaph; vide, vis: video,
      vision, visible; Suffix examples: ile: juvenile,
      senile, missile; nomy: autonomy, economy,
      taxonomy; some: lonesome, threesome, gruesome;
      tude: gratitude, aptitude, multitude

Turn downtime into learning time!

Other books in the

Daily *Warm-Ups* series:

- Algebra
- Algebra II
- Analogies
- Biology
- Character Education
- Chemistry
- Commonly Confused Words
- Critical Thinking
- Earth Science
- Geography
- Geometry
- Journal Writing
- Mythology

- Physics
- Poetry
- Pre-Algebra
- Shakespeare
- Spelling & Grammar
- Test-Prep Words
- U.S. History
- Vocabulary
- World Cultures
- World History
- World Religions
- Writing